Accident prevention
on board ship at sea and in port

GW00538261

An ILO code of practice

Accident prevention on board ship at sea and in port

International Labour Office   Geneva

ILO
Accident prevention on board ship at sea and in port. An ILO code of practice.
Geneva, International Labour Office, 2nd edition, 1996

/Code of practice/, /Occupational safety/, /Seafarer/, /Persons employed on board ship/, /Port/. 13.04.2
ISBN 92-2-109450-2

Also published in Spanish: *Prevención de accidents a bordo de los buques en el mar y en los puertos.* Repertorio de recomendaciones prácticas (ISBN 92-2-309450-X), Geneva, 1996

Also published in French: *Prévention des accidents à bord des navires en mer et dans les ports.* Recueil de directives pratiques (ISBN 92-2-209450-6), Geneva, 1996

ILO Cataloguing in Publication Data

Printed in Switzerland

Preface

In accordance with the decision taken by the Governing Body of the ILO at its 254th Session (November 1992), a Meeting of Experts was convened in Geneva from 28 September to 5 October 1993 to revise the ILO Code of Practice on Accident Prevention on Board Ship at Sea and in Port. The Meeting was composed of 15 experts, five appointed following consultations with governments, five following consultations with the Employers' group and five following consultations with the Workers' group of the Governing Body.[1] After examining and finalizing the text, based on a draft prepared by the Office, the experts adopted this code.

---

[1] *Experts appointed following consultations with governments:*

Mr. L. D. Barchue, Sr. (Liberia), Deputy Permanent Representative to the IMO, Permanent Mission of the Republic of Liberia to the International Maritime Organization (IMO).

Mr. A. Flatrud (Norway), Director of Department, Norwegian Maritime Directorate.

Captain H. Matsuda (Japan), Director, Employment Security Office, Administration Division, Seafarers' Department, Maritime Technology and Safety Bureau, Ministry of Transport.

Mr. W. Rabe (United States), Deputy Chief, Marine Investigation Division, Commandant (G-MMI), United States Coast Guard.

> *Adviser:* Mr. C. Young, Marine Transportation Specialist, Commandant (G-MVP-4), United States Coast Guard.

Ms. E. A. Snow (United Kingdom), Higher Executive Officer, Occupational Health and Safety (Seafarers), Marine Directorate, Surveyor-General's Organization, Department of Transport.

Experts appointed following consultations with the Employers' group of the Governing Body:

Captain K. Akatsuka (Japan), General Manager, Japanese Shipowners' Association.

Captain K. R. Damkjaer (Denmark), Head of Division, Danish Shipowners' Association.

Mr. G. Koltsidopoulos (Greece), Legal Adviser, Union of Greek Shipowners.

The experts considered that the code of practice constituted a body of advice which would be of great value to ILO member States. The code should not be regarded as a legally binding instrument, and was not intended to supersede national laws or regulations or other national safety and health rules. Its practical recommendations are intended for use by all those who have responsibility for safety and health on board ship. Its object is to provide guidance to shipowners and seafarers and others concerned with the framing of provisions of this kind in both the public and private sectors.

Captain M. R. Lowle (United Kingdom), Manager, Health, Safety and Environment, Shell Tankers (UK) Ltd.

Captain C. J. Park (Republic of Korea), General Manager, Marine Dept., Korea Shipowners' Association.

Experts appointed following consultations with the Workers' group of the Governing Body:

Mr. L. Dolleris (Denmark), President, Maskinmestrenes Forening [Union of Chief Engineers].

Mr. N. McVicar (United Kingdom), National Organizer RMT, National Union of Rail, Maritime and Transport Workers.

Mr. H. Rodriguez Navarrete (Chile), Secretary-General, Chilean Seafarers' Federation (FETRICH).

Mr. A Papaconstuntinos (Australia), Joint National Secretary, Maritime Union of Australia.

Mr. T. Tay (Singapore), General Secretary, Singapore Maritime Officers' Union.

Observers from member States:

Mr. E. H. Salman (Bahrain), Harbour Operation Officer, Directorate General of Ports, Harbour Section.

Mr. S. R. Sanad (Bahrain), Official, Ministry of Finance.

Mr. E. Hosannah (Brazil), First Secretary, Permanent Mission of Brazil in Geneva.

Mr. G. Boubopoulos (Greece), Lieutenant HCG, Seaman's Labour Division – Hellenic Coast Guard, Ministry of Mercantile Marine.

Mr. F. Wakaki (Japan), Counsellor, Permanent Mission of Japan in Geneva.

Ms. L. Vallarino (Panama), Ambassador, Permanent Mission of Panama in Geneva.

Intergovernmental organizations represented:

Commission of the European Communities (CEC): Mr. L. Dutailly.

It may be impracticable to apply some of these recommendations to a particular ship or type of shipping operation. In such cases, every endeavour should be made to observe the intent of the recommendations, and the risks that may be involved in any operation covered by the code should be taken into consideration when applying these measures.

A code such as this cannot cover every aspect of safety both at work and in off-duty periods aboard ship at sea and in port, and no human activity is free from some measure of risk. Accidents are in many cases caused by lack of knowledge or inadequate training, incomplete understanding of ships and ship operations, non-adherence to procedures, lack of foresight and the taking of unnecessary risks, often in quite simple operations. Prudence and foresight are natural characteristics of the good seafarer at work, who should make it a habit to be on the lookout for the hazards in any situation, including ordinary everyday situations.

Non-governmental organizations represented:

International Confederation of Free Trade Unions (ICFTU): Mr. G. Ryder, Mr. D. Cunniah.

International Organization of Employers (IOE): Ms. B. Perkins.

International Organization for Standardization (ISO): Mr. R. R. Spencer, Mr. F. Abram.

International Shipping Federation (ISF): Mr. D. Dearsley, Captain F. M. Marchant.

International Transport Workers' Federation (ITF): Mr. J. P. Whitlow.

World Federation of Trade Unions (WFTU): Mr. A. Potapov.

ILO representatives:

Mr. B. K. Nilssen, Chief, Maritime Industries Branch, ILO.

Mr. D. Appave, Maritime Industries Branch, ILO.

Mr. B. Wagner, Maritime Industries Branch, ILO.

Ms. T. Bezat-Powell, Multisectoral Support Section, ILO.

ILO consultant:

Captain I. Lavery, Research and Consultancy services, University of Ulster, United Kingdom.

Much of the information contained in this code has been taken from national codes of practice and safety-related publications. Since the guidelines cannot cover every aspect of safety and health on board ships, a list of publications and other information is appended to the code.

The experts recognized that some countries and shipping companies had established more progressive safety and health policies and programmes than those prescribed in this code. The experts fully supported these developments and encouraged others to emulate these initiatives.

Throughout the code there are references to ILO and International Maritime Organization (IMO) instruments, resolutions and publications and to publications of other intergovernmental and non-governmental organizations. Whenever such instruments, resolutions and publications are utilized, it should be ensured that the most recent applicable editions or versions are consulted.

The text of the code was approved for publication by the Governing Body of the ILO at its 261st Session (November 1994).

Contents

Accident prevention on board ship

Contents

1. General provisions

1.1. Objective

1.1.1. The objective of this code is to provide practical guidance on safety and health in shipboard work with a view to:

(a) preventing accidents, diseases and other harmful effects on the health of seafarers arising from employment on board ship at sea and in port;

(b) ensuring that the responsibility for safety and health is understood and remains a priority for all concerned with maritime transport, including governments, shipowners and seafarers; and

(c) promoting consultation and cooperation among governments, as well as shipowners' and seafarers' organizations in the improvement of safety and health on board ship.

1.1.2. The code also provides guidance in the implementation of the provisions of the Prevention of Occupational Accidents to Seafarers Convention, 1970 (No. 134), and Recommendation, 1970 (No. 142), as well as other applicable ILO Conventions and Recommendations.

1.2. Application

1.2.1. The code covers the safety and health of all seafarers serving on board all seagoing ships, whether publicly or privately owned, and which are ordinarily engaged in commercial maritime navigation. However, parts of the code may be applicable to vessels used in inland waterways or to fishing vessels.

1.2.2. The provisions of this code should be considered as the basic minimum requirements for protecting seafarers' safety and health.

1.3. General definitions[1]

1.3.1. For the purposes of this code the following terms have been defined as follows:

(a) *competent authority:* a minister, government department or other authority having power to issue regulations, orders or other instructions having the force of law in respect of safety and health aboard any vessel registered in their territory or any ship within their territorial waters and ports;

(b) *competent person or competent officer:* a rating or an officer possessing adequate qualifications, such as suitable training and sufficient knowledge, experience and skill, and including, where appropriate, any certificates required by the competent authority, to fill a particular position, carry out a specific task, or assume supervisory responsibility. The competent authority may define appropriate criteria for the designation of such persons and may determine the duties assigned to them;[2]

(c) *crew:* seafarers, other than the master, working on the ship;

(d) *officer:* one who is ranked as an officer by national laws or regulations;[3]

(e) *personal protective equipment:* includes but is not limited to protective clothing, safety helmets, eye and face protection, hearing protection, gloves, safety footwear, lifelines, safety harnesses, breathing apparatus and respirators, as appropriate;

---

[1] Use of the male gender in the text should be read as meaning male or female.

[2] Such standards should at least be those of the IMO's International Convention on Standards of Training, Certification and Watchkeeping for Seafarers, 1978 (and any subsequent revisions or amendments), and the requirements of the ILO's Merchant Shipping (Minimum Standards) Convention, 1976 (No. 147), and other relevant instruments.

[3] See also 1.3.1(b), above.

(f) *rating:* a competent member of the crew other than an officer;

(g) *responsible persons:* persons having authority delegated to them either directly or indirectly by the shipowner or the master to carry out or supervise the duties or operations under consideration;

(h) *safety officer:* an officer designated by the shipowner or the master as being responsible for carrying out certain tasks associated with shipboard safety and health;

(i) *safety policy:* a written document produced by a shipowner indicating in broad terms his commitment, aims and objectives;

(j) *safety programme:* a detailed plan designed to implement the ideals and intentions expressed in the safety policy;

(k) *safety representative:* a member of the crew elected or appointed by and from the members of the crew to serve on the shipboard safety and health committee;

(l) *shipboard safety and health committee:* a committee which examines and deals with all aspects of shipboard safety and health and related issues;

(m) *seafarer:* any person employed in any capacity on board a seagoing ship or vessel engaged in commercial maritime navigation, whether publicly or privately owned, other than a ship of war;

(n) *ship or vessel:* any seagoing registered craft, whether publicly or privately owned, engaged in commercial maritime navigation;

(o) *shipowner:* any person(s) or organization that owns the ship or acts on behalf of the owner and is responsible for the ship and its equipment or for the seafarers employed thereon. For the purposes of the code, the term may also include, for example, a ship management company.

2. General duties and responsibilities

2.1. General duties of the competent authority of flag States

2.1.1. The competent authority should, on the basis of an assessment of safety and health hazards and in consultation with shipowners' and seafarers' organizations, adopt national laws or regulations to ensure the safety and health of seafarers working on ships.

2.1.2. A practical application of these national laws or regulations should be provided through technical standards or codes of practice, or by other appropriate methods.

2.1.3. In giving effect to paragraphs 2.1.1 and 2.1.2 above, the competent authority should have due regard to the relevant standards adopted by recognized international organizations in the field of maritime safety.[1]

2.1.4. The competent authority should provide appropriate inspection services to enforce or administer the application of the provisions of national laws and regulations and should provide the

---

[1] These include, from the International Labour Organization, the Merchant Shipping (Minimum Standards) Convention, 1976 (No. 147); the Prevention of Accidents (Seafarers) Convention, 1970 (No. 134); the Prevention of Accidents (Seafarers) Recommendation, 1970 (No. 142); and from the International Maritime Organization, the International Convention for the Safety of Life at Sea, 1974 (SOLAS); the International Convention on Standards of Training, Certification and Watchkeeping for Seafarers, 1978 (STCW); the International Convention on Loadlines, 1966 (ICL); the Convention on the International Regulations for Preventing Collisions at Sea, 1972 (COLREG) and any subsequent revisions of the above instruments.

necessary resources for the accomplishment of their task, or satisfy itself that appropriate inspection and enforcement are carried out.[1]

2.1.5. The inspection and survey of ships should normally be carried out by the competent authority.[2] If inspection and survey are delegated to classification societies and other bodies, the competent authority should ensure that its international obligations[3] are fulfilled and that national laws and regulations are enforced.

2.1.6. The measures to be taken to ensure organized cooperation between shipowners and seafarers to promote safety and health on board ship should be prescribed by national law or regulations or by the competent authority.[4] Such measures may include but should not be limited to:

(a) the establishment on each ship of a safety and health committee with well-defined powers and duties;

(b) the appointment of an elected seafarers' safety representative(s) with well-defined powers and responsibilities; and

(c) the appointment by the shipowner or master of a suitably qualified and experienced officer to promote safety and health.

---

[1] For guidance on inspections in accordance with Convention No. 147, the ILO publication *Inspection of labour conditions on board ship: Guide-lines for procedure* should be followed. In accordance with Article 2 of Convention No. 134, the competent authority in each maritime country shall take the necessary measures to ensure that occupational accidents are adequately reported and investigated, and comprehensive statistics on such accidents kept and analysed. Use may also be made of the IMO/ILO Guidelines for the investigation of accidents where fatigue may have been a contributing factor, where appropriate.

[2] See also the Labour Inspection (Seamen) Recommendation, 1926 (No. 28).

[3] Guidelines for the Authorization of Organizations Acting on Behalf of the Administration, IMO Resolution A.739(18), 1993, and subsequent related resolutions should be followed.

[4] The Occupational Safety and Health Recommendation, 1981 (No. 164), calls for the formation of safety committees and specifies the rights of the committee and its members. Article 7 of the Prevention of Accidents (Seafarers) Convention, 1970 (No. 134), provides for the appointment, from amongst the crew, of a suitable committee responsible, under the master, for accident prevention.

2.1.7. When comparable national laws or regulations are in place to address the concern in paragraph 2.1.6, the competent authority should ensure that the organization and execution of these measures are not less effective than as recommended above.

2.1.8. The competent authority should take immediate action to investigate and, where appropriate, take measures to have deficiencies relating to ships registered in its territory corrected, as reported by the competent authorities of other States.

2.1.9. Where the safety of the ship or the safety and health of the crew are endangered, the competent authority should, in accordance with national laws and regulations, take effective measures to ensure that the ship is prohibited from leaving port until such deficiencies have been remedied and compliance with the relevant laws and regulations assured.

2.1.10. The competent authority should establish laws and regulations on requirements for medical facilities and procedures, and for the medical training of shipboard personnel as appropriate. Due regard should be given to the relevant ILO instruments. [1] Every ship should be required to carry on board the *International medical guide for ships* or an equivalent national guide.

2.1.11. The competent authority should ensure that seafarers employed on board ships registered in its territory are properly certificated, where required. Due regard should be given to relevant ILO and IMO instruments, guidelines, resolutions and publications, in particular the revised *ILO/IMO Document for guidance: An international maritime training guide* (1985)[2] and any subsequent revisions.

---

[1] In particular, the Health Protection and Medical Care (Seafarers) Convention, 1987 (No. 164).

[2] Which takes into account the International Convention on Standards of Training, Certification and Watchkeeping for Seafarers, 1978, as well as other ILO and IMO instruments, resolutions and publications.

2.2. General duties and responsibilities of competent authorities other than the flag State

2.2.1. Where duties require the application by a competent authority other than the flag State, due account should be taken of the relevant principles of international law.

2.3. General duties and responsibilities of shipowners

2.3.1. Generally, the shipowner is primarily responsible for the safety and health of all seafarers on board ship. However, the day-to-day responsibility generally lies with the master, who should observe the shipowners' reporting procedures. Shipowners should provide adequate means and organization and should establish a suitable policy on the safety and health of seafarers consistent with international and national laws and regulations. The policy and programme should set out the responsibilities of all relevant parties, including onshore staff and any subcontracting companies.[1]

2.3.2. The development of the necessary degree of safety consciousness and the achievement of high standards of safety depend on foresight, good organization and the wholehearted support of management and of all seafarers. Therefore, shipowners should consult with seafarers' organizations with regard to the safety and health policy.

2.3.3. Shipowners should ensure that design of their ships takes account of ergonomic principles and conforms to relevant international and national laws, regulations, standards or codes of practice.

---

[1] Such a policy should be based on the International Management Code for the Safe Operation of Ships and for Pollution Prevention (International Safety for Management (ISM) Code), IMO Assembly Resolution A.741(18), 1993, and any subsequent revisions.

2.3.4. Shipowners should provide and maintain ships, equipment, tools, operating manuals and other documentation, and organize all planning and operations in such a manner that, as far as is reasonably practicable there is no risk of accident or injury to seafarers. In particular, activities should be planned, prepared and undertaken so that:

(a) dangers likely to arise on board ship are prevented;

(b) excessively or unnecessarily strenuous work positions and movements are avoided;

(c) organization of all work takes into account the safety and health of seafarers;

(d) materials and products are used safely and pose no danger to seafarers' health; and

(e) working methods are employed which protect seafarers against the harmful effects of chemical, physical and biological agents.

2.3.5. Shipowners should observe the appropriate national and international laws when deciding manning levels, and take into account the necessary standards of fitness, state of health, experience, competence and language skills to ensure the safety and health of seafarers in the performance of their duties and responsibilities when operating on board. In doing so the shipowners should:

(a) take account of the links between shipboard safety and acceptable working and living conditions, including working hours, rest periods, bedding, mess utensils, adequate accommodation and nutrition;[1]

---

[1] The ILO's Seafarers' Welfare at Sea and in Port Convention, 1987 (No. 163), and Recommendation, 1987 (No. 173); the Merchant Shipping (Minimum Standards) Convention, 1976 (No. 147); and the Bedding, Mess Utensils and Miscellaneous Provisions (Ships' Crews) Recommendation, 1946 (No. 78).

(b) verify that the seafarer holds appropriate medical and competency certificates and endeavour to confirm their validity;

(c) recognize fatigue as a potential hazard to safety and health, therefore operations on ships should be planned to take into account
the expected period of work and the prevailing conditions on
board in order to minimize fatigue;[1]

(d) where circumstances do not allow adequate rest periods for seafarers, either the crew complement should be supplemented or
the vessel's work programme should be reassigned; and

(e) take account of reports and recommendations made by the master or safety committee regarding adequacy of numbers of
seafarers, their degree of competence and skills required for
accident-free operation of the ship.

2.3.6. Shipowners should provide such supervision as will ensure that seafarers perform their work with due regard to their safety
and health. Shipowners should direct the master and the master should
instruct the officers that the work of all on board will be organized in
such a way as to avoid unnecessary risks to safety and health. Shipowners should make masters and seafarers fully aware of all activities on board that could affect their safety and health.

2.3.7. Shipowners should arrange for a designated person from
shoreside operations, preferably a person at the highest possible level
within the management structure, to:

(a) consult closely with the master and crew on all matters concerning safety and health;

(b) review the reports of shipboard safety and health committees
and consider any suggested improvements and other feedback
information received from the ship; and

(c) monitor the performance of equipment and personnel.

---

[1] See IMO Resolution A.772(18), 1993, on Fatigue Factors in Manning and Safety.

2.3.8. Shipowners should establish safety and health committees on board ships or make other suitable arrangements consistent with national laws and regulations for the participation of seafarers in the establishment of safe working conditions. The duties and responsibilities of such committees, as well as those of designated safety representatives, are described below in section 2.6. When drawing up procedures concerning safety and health committees and safety representatives, shipowners should consult the relevant seafarers' organizations.

2.3.9. Shipowners should arrange for regular safety inspections of all parts of their ships by competent persons at suitable intervals. The inspection should also include tools, equipment and machinery on which the safety of the seafarers may depend. Precautions should be taken in performing the inspection, for example, ensuring that tanks are ventilated or gas freed. Such inspections should, as a minimum, comply with any national requirements.

2.3.10. Shipowners should ensure that, before taking on their responsibilities, all seafarers are suitably instructed in the hazards connected with their work and the shipboard environment and trained in the precautions which must be taken to avoid accidents and injury to health. The training should address day-to-day shipboard operations as well as contingency planning and emergency preparedness. A training manual containing information and instructions on life-saving appliances and survival methods should be kept in each mess room and recreation room or in each cabin.[1] The manual should be written in easily understood terms and illustrated wherever possible.

2.3.11. Shipowners should take all practicable steps to ensure that, before taking on their responsibilities, seafarers are made aware of the relevant national and international laws, regulations, standards,

---

[1] A requirement found in Chapter III of the Annex to the International Convention for the Safety of Life at Sea (1974), as amended.

codes of practice, instructions and advice relating to the prevention of accidents and injuries to health. The linguistic abilities of the seafarers should be taken into account in the dissemination of material.

2.3.12. Shipowners should provide appropriate medical equipment and trained personnel in accordance with national laws and regulations (see paragraph 2.1.10). The *International medical guide for ships*, or a national equivalent, should be carried on board.

2.3.13. Shipowners should report occupational accidents, diseases and dangerous occurrences to the competent authority in accordance with national laws and regulations. All accidents to seafarers resulting in loss of life or serious injury should be reported forthwith to the competent authority[1] and an investigation of these accidents should be carried out (see Chapter 3). Other injuries resulting in incapacity from work for periods of time as may be specified in national laws or regulations, as well as prescribed occupational diseases, should be reported to the competent authority within such time and in such form as may be specified.

2.3.14. Shipowners should investigate all accidents and near accidents, analyse their underlying causes and convey what is learned throughout the company as appropriate. Shipowners should also consider establishing a near-accident reporting system.

2.3.15. Shipowners should encourage seafarers to report all unsafe and unhealthy conditions or operations.

2.3.16. Shipowners should provide each ship with the necessary equipment, manuals and other information to ensure that all operations are carried out in such a manner as to reduce to a minimum any adverse effects on seafarers' safety and health.

---

[1] As required by the ILO's Prevention of Accidents (Seafarers) Convention, 1970 (No. 134).

2.3.17. Shipowners should provide proper information to the seafarers regarding safety and health hazards and measures related to the work processes. This information should be presented in a form and language which crew members can easily understand.

2.4. General duties and responsibilities of the master

2.4.1. The master should implement the shipowner's safety and health policy and programme on board the ship. The policy and programme, including safety rules and instructions, should be clearly communicated to all members of the crew. The master should ensure that work carried out on or from the ship is carried out in such a way as to avoid the possibility of accidents and the exposure of seafarers to conditions which may lead to injury or damage to their health.

2.4.2. The master should ensure that any work requiring several seafarers to work together and which poses special hazards is supervised by a competent person.

2.4.3. The master should ensure that seafarers are assigned only to work to which they are suited by age, state of health and skills.

2.4.4. The master should ensure that no young person is assigned to inappropriate duties.[1]

2.4.5. The master should issue appropriate notices and instructions in a clear and easily understood manner, in a language or languages understood by the entire crew and verify, as appropriate, that such instructions have been understood.

---

[1] Protection of Young Seafarers Recommendation, 1976 (No. 153).

2.4.6. The master should ensure, in compliance with national laws and regulations, as well as collective agreements, where they exist, that all crew on board have:

(a) a tolerable workload;

(b) reasonable hours of work;

(c) reasonable rest periods during working hours, having special regard to work which is strenuous, hazardous or monotonous; and

(d) rest days at reasonable intervals.

2.4.7. The master should investigate all accidents or near accidents and record and report them in compliance with national laws and regulations and the shipowner's reporting procedures (see Chapter 3).

2.4.8. The master should ensure the availability of operating manuals, vessel plans, national laws and regulations, safety procedures and other such information to those seafarers who need such information to conduct their work safely. In particular, the master should ensure that any necessary instructions and notices concerning the safety and health of the crew are posted in prominent and suitable places or brought to the crew's attention by other effective means.

2.4.9. Where shipboard safety and health committees are established, the master should hold regular meetings of the committee, at intervals of 4-6 weeks or as required, and ensure that the reports of the committee are given due consideration.

2.4.10. The master should ensure that safety equipment, including all emergency and protective equipment, is maintained in good order and stowed properly.

2.4.11. The master should ensure that all statutory drills and musters are carried out realistically, effectively and conscientiously at the required intervals and in compliance with any applicable rules and regulations.[1]

2.4.12. The master should ensure that practice and training are given in emergency procedures. The use of any special emergency equipment should be demonstrated to the crew at regular intervals.

2.4.13. Unless contrary to national law or practice, the master should ensure that one or more designated persons are assigned to serve as safety officer (duties described in section 2.7).

2.4.14. The master should institute the "permit-to-work" system on board ship (see Chapter 4).

2.5. General duties and responsibilities of seafarers

2.5.1. Seafarers should participate in ensuring safe working conditions and should be encouraged to express views on working procedures adopted as they may affect safety and health, without fear of dismissal or other prejudicial measures.

2.5.2. Seafarers should have the right to remove themselves from dangerous situations or operations when they have good reason to believe that there is an imminent and serious danger to their safety and health. In such circumstances, the competent officer should be informed of the danger forthwith and seafarers should be protected from undue consequences, in accordance with national conditions and practice.[2]

---

[1] At the very least in compliance with Chapter III of the Annex to SOLAS (1974), as amended.

[2] Based upon Article 13 of the Occupational Safety and Health Convention, 1981 (No. 155).

2.5.3. Notwithstanding paragraph 2.5.2., seafarers should only abandon ship on the express order of the master or, in his absence, the competent person next in line of authority.

2.5.4. Seafarers should:

(a) cooperate as closely as possible with the shipowner in the application of the prescribed safety and health measures;

(b) take care of their own safety and health and of other persons who may be affected by their acts or omissions at work;

(c) use and take care of personal protective equipment and clothing at their disposal and not misuse any means provided for their own protection or the protection of others;

(d) report forthwith to their immediate supervisor any situation which they believe could pose a hazard and which they cannot properly deal with themselves;

(e) comply with the prescribed safety and health measures; and

(f) participate in safety and health meetings.

2.5.5. Except in an emergency, seafarers, unless duly authorized, should not interfere with, remove, or displace any safety device or other equipment and appliances furnished for their protection or the protection of others, or interfere with any method or process adopted with a view to preventing accidents and injury to health.

2.5.6. Seafarers should not operate or interfere with equipment which they have not been duly authorized to operate, maintain or use.

2.5.7. A seafarer who gives an order or otherwise instructs another seafarer should be certain that the order or instructions are understood.

2.5.8. If a seafarer does not fully understand an order, instruction or any other communication from another seafarer, clarification should be sought.

2.5.9. Seafarers have a duty to be particularly diligent during fire, lifeboat and other drills and emergency training.

2.5.10. The crew should implement the shipowner's safety and health policy and programme as delegated to them by the master in a diligent and professional manner and demonstrate their full support for shipboard safety. They should do everything in their power to maintain their own health and safety as well as the health and safety of other crew members and other persons on board.

2.6. General duties and responsibilities of the shipboard safety and health committee

2.6.1. A safety and health committee should assist in the implementation of the shipowner's safety and health policy and programme and provide seafarers with a forum to influence safety and health matters, in accordance with paragraph 2.1.6.

2.6.2. The safety and health committee should as a minimum consist of officers and ratings who should be appointed or elected as appropriate, bearing in mind the importance of balanced representation by shipboard departments and functions.

2.6.3. All members of the safety and health committee should be given adequate information, e.g. in writing and by audio-visual materials, etc., on safety and health matters.

2.6.4. The duties and responsibilities of the safety and health committee include but are not limited to:

(a) ensuring that the competent authority's and the shipowner's safety and health requirements are complied with;

(b) making representations and recommendations on behalf of the crew through the master to the shipowner;

(c) discussing and taking appropriate action in respect of any safety and health matters affecting the crew, and the evaluation of adequate protective and safety equipment, including life-saving equipment; and

(d) studying accident reports.

2.6.5. A record should be kept of all committee meetings and copies should be posted for viewing by the entire crew. A copy should be sent to the person ashore designated by the shipowner as responsible for ship safety.

2.6.6. Committee members should not be subject to dismissal or other prejudicial measures for carrying out functions assigned to this role.

2.6.7. The safety and health committee should be consulted during the planning or alteration of shipboard work processes which may affect safety and health.

2.6.8. The safety and health committee should have access to information on hazards or potential hazards on board which are known to the shipowner and master, including information on hazardous or dangerous cargoes. The committee members should have access to the *International Maritime Dangerous Goods Code* and other relevant IMO publications.

2.6.9. Committee members should be given reasonable time within working hours to exercise their safety functions, including attendance at safety and health committee meetings.

2.7. General duties and responsibilities of the safety officer

2.7.1. Unless contrary to national law or practice, the safety officer should implement the shipowner's safety and health policy and programme and carry out the instructions of the master to:

(a) improve the crew's safety awareness;

(b) investigate any safety complaints brought to his or her attention and report the same to the safety and health committee and to the individual, where necessary;

(c)   investigate accidents and make the appropriate recommendations to prevent the recurrence of such accidents;

(d)   carry out safety and health inspections; and

(e)   monitor and carry out the on-board safety training of seafarers.

2.7.2.   Whenever possible, the safety officer should seek the cooperation and assistance of the safety and health committee and the safety representative(s) and others in carrying out these duties.

2.8. General duties and responsibilities of the safety representative(s)

2.8.1.   Unless contrary to national law or practice, the safety representative(s) should represent the crew on matters affecting their safety and health.

2.8.2.   In carrying out the role of safety representative, access to information, assistance and advice should be provided, where necessary, by the safety committee, the shipowner and professional bodies including workers' organizations.[1]

2.8.3.   The safety representative(s):

(a)   should be elected or appointed by and from the crew, in accordance with paragraph 2.6.2, and should participate in meetings of the safety and health committee;

(b)   should not be subject to dismissal or other prejudicial measures for carrying out functions assigned to this role.

---

[1] See the ILO's Freedom of Association and Protection of the Right to Organize Convention, 1948 (No. 87), Right to Organize and Collective Bargaining Convention, 1949 (No. 98), and Merchant Shipping (Minimum Standards) Convention, 1976 (No. 147).

2.8.4. The safety representative(s) should:

(a) have access to all parts of the ship;

(b) participate in the investigation of accidents and near-accidents;

(c) have access to all the necessary documentation, including investigation reports, past minutes of safety and health committees, etc.; and

(d) receive appropriate training.

3. Reporting of accidents

3.1. General provisions

3.1.1. The principal purpose of accident investigation, reporting and analysis should be to minimize the potential for a recurrence of such accidents.

3.1.2. The cause or causes of all accidents or near accidents should be investigated by the ship's safety officer.

3.1.3. A full report of any incident should be made to the safety and health committee and, through the master, to the appropriate persons ashore. Shipowners should report occupational accidents and diseases to the competent authority in accordance with paragraph 2.3.13.

3.1.4. Reports of accidents and near accidents should be discussed at safety and health committee meetings on board ship and steps should be taken to minimize the possibility of recurrences. The reports should also be discussed by shore management, and, if necessary, the shipowner's safety and health policy should be amended to take account of the conclusions of the investigation.

4. Permit-to-work systems

4.1. General provisions

4.1.1. The permit-to-work system is a method whereby safety procedures are specified in writing on a form issued to seafarers who are entrusted with a task which may involve work of a hazardous nature.

4.1.2. Permits should only be used for the more hazardous tasks and the system should not become over-complicated.

4.1.3. The form should describe the work to be carried out and the necessary safety precautions. All foreseeable hazards should be considered, a predetermined safe procedure should be adopted and the appropriate precautions should be written down in a correct sequence.

4.1.4. The permit should contain a carefully planned checklist to identify, control or eliminate hazards and should state the emergency procedure in the event of an accident.

4.1.5. A permit should be issued only by an officer with experience in the work operation. The officer should ensure that the checks have been properly carried out and, together with the person in charge, sign the permit only when satisfied that it is safe for the work to proceed. The master should countersign any such permits.

4.1.6. Procedures for locking off at points of isolation and signing for, and the subsequent cancellation of, permits and "making live" should be covered.

4.1.7. A sample permit is included in Appendix 1.

5. General shipboard safety and health considerations

5.1. Shipboard housekeeping and personal health and hygiene

5.1.1. The importance of good housekeeping in the prevention of accidents and conditions likely to be injurious to health should be given proper priority in the training of every member of the crew until its acceptance becomes second nature.

5.1.2. Minor deficiencies in the structure, equipment or furnishings (for example, protruding nails and screws, loose fittings and handles, uneven and damaged flooring, rough and splintered edges to woodwork and jamming doors) may cause cuts, bruises, trips and falls. They should be repaired as soon as they are noticed.

5.1.3. Any spillage of oil or other substance likely to cause a hazard should be removed immediately.

5.1.4. Accumulations of ice, snow or slush should be removed from working areas and passages on deck.

5.1.5. If asbestos-containing panels, cladding or insulation work loose or are damaged in the course of a voyage, the exposed edges or surfaces should be protected pending proper repair by a suitable coating or covering to prevent asbestos fibres from being released and dispersed into the air. Known asbestos-containing materials should only be disturbed for the purpose of essential maintenance and then only in strict compliance with national or international requirements, as appropriate. In general, the use of asbestos insulating material should be prohibited. (See also paragraph 17.5.5.)

5.1.6. Flickering lights may indicate faults in wiring or fittings which may lead to electric shocks or fires. They should be investigated and repaired by a competent person. Failed light bulbs should be replaced as soon as possible.

5.1.7. Instruction plates, notices and operating indicators should be kept clean and legible.

5.1.8. Heavy objects, particularly if placed at a height above deck level, should be stowed securely against the movement of the ship. Similarly, furniture and other objects likely to fall or shift during heavy weather should be properly stowed or secured.

5.1.9. Doors, whether open or closed, should be properly secured.

5.1.10. Coils of rope and wires on deck should be located so as not to pose a tripping hazard.

5.1.11. Under no circumstances whatsoever should seafarers stand in a bight of a rope or wire which is lying on deck. Seafarers should never stand or move across a rope or wire that is under strain.

5.1.12. Ropes and wires are frequently under strain during mooring operations and seafarers should, as much as possible, always stand in a place of safety from whiplash should ropes or wires break.

5.1.13. The stowage and dispersal of deck or machinery equipment should be well planned and organized so that each item has its proper place.

5.1.14. Seafarers should always stand clear of any load being lifted and should not walk close to or underneath any load being lifted or while it is suspended.

5.1.15. Litter presents a fire risk and may cause slips, falls or conceal other hazards. It should be disposed of in compliance with the appropriate MARPOL legislation.[1]

5.1.16. Tasks should be carried out with account being taken of possible risks to other persons; for example, water from hosing down the deck may enter other spaces and result in slips and falls.

5.1.17. Aerosols having volatile and inflammable content should never be used or placed near naked flames or other heat sources even when empty.

5.1.18. (1) Seafarers should have appropriate and up-to-date vaccinations and inoculations.

(2) Small cuts and abrasions should be treated immediately.

(3) Precautions should be taken to avoid insect bites. In particular, anti-malaria precautions should be taken before, during and after the ship visits ports where malaria is known to exist.

5.1.19. High standards of personal cleanliness and hygiene should be maintained at all times. Washing facilities should be provided in toilets. Hands should always be well washed after using paints or after possible exposure to toxic substances.

5.1.20. Working in conditions of high humidity and heat may cause heat exhaustion or heat stroke. Sensible precautions should be taken, including the drinking of sufficient water and the taking of additional salt, if appropriate.

5.1.21. Seafarers should protect themselves from the sun in tropical areas and be informed that prolonged sun bathing, even when the skin is protected, may be harmful.

5.1.22. Seafarers should be made aware of the health hazards related to smoking.

---

[1] International Convention for the Prevention of Pollution from Ships (MARPOL), 1973, as amended by the Protocol of 1978, Annexes I and V, and related resolutions.

5.2. Use of chemicals[1]

5.2.1. Toxic and other hazardous substances and products should be used and stored in such a way that users and others are safeguarded against accidents, injuries or particular discomfort.

5.2.2. A record (product data sheet) should, when obtainable, be kept on board, available to all users, containing sufficient information to determine the degree of the danger posed by the substances.

5.2.3. If possible, the substance should be stored in the original packaging or in another correspondingly labelled packaging that cannot give rise to confusion. Such substances must be stored in a locked, well-ventilated room.

5.2.4. Chemicals should always be handled with extreme care, protection should be worn and the manufacturer's instructions closely followed. Particular attention should be paid to protecting eyes.

5.2.5. Some cleaning agents, such as caustic soda and bleach, are chemicals and may burn the skin. A chemical from an unlabelled container should never be used.

5.2.6. Exposure to certain substances such as mineral oils, natural solvents and chemicals, including domestic cleaning agents and detergents, may cause dermatitis. Suitable gloves should be worn when using such substances and the owner should provide suitable barrier creams which may help to protect the skin.

5.2.7. The IMO/WHO/ILO Medical First Aid Guide should be consulted for accidents involving chemicals.

---

[1] Reference may be made to *Safety and health in the use of chemicals at work: A training manual*, by A. Bakar Che Man and D. Gold (Geneva, 1992), or a similar guide.

5.3. Fire prevention

5.3.1. Smoking[1]

5.3.1.1. Smoking should be permitted only in authorized areas, and instructions and prohibition notices should be prominently displayed.

5.3.1.2. Careless disposal of burning matches and cigarette ends is dangerous: ashtrays, or other suitable containers, should be provided and used in locations where smoking is permitted.

5.3.1.3. Seafarers should be made aware of the dangers of smoking in bed.

5.3.2. Electrical and other fittings

5.3.2.1. Unauthorized persons should not interfere with electrical equipment and fittings.

5.3.2.2. All electrical faults in equipment, fittings or wiring should be reported immediately to the appropriate responsible person.

5.3.2.3. The overloading of a circuit should not be permitted as it can cause fires.

5.3.2.4. Portable heaters carried as ship's equipment should not be used except in exceptional circumstances and with due warning of their accompanying dangers.

5.3.2.5. Personal heating appliances should not be used under any circumstances.

---

[1] See Chapter 24 for special provisions concerning smoking on tankers.

5.3.2.6. All portable electrical appliances should be isolated from the mains when not in use.

5.3.2.7. All personal electrical equipment in accommodation areas should be connected only by standard plugs fitting into the sockets provided.

5.3.2.8. Extension leads and multi-socket plugs should not be used in accommodation areas for connecting several items of electrical equipment to one plug or socket.

5.3.2.9. When seafarers use portable equipment or portable lamps they should ensure that any flexible cables passing through doors, hatches, manholes, etc., are protected and that their insulation is not damaged by the closing of doors, covers or lids.

5.3.2.10. Seafarers should not site private aerials in the vicinity of the vessel's aerials.

5.3.2.11. Seafarers should not attempt to work on or repair their personal mains-powered radios, compact disc players or other equipment without removing the mains plug, and should have the equipment checked by a competent person before plugging it in again.

5.3.2.12. Wall charts giving instructions on emergency first-aid treatment to seafarers who have suffered electric shock should be displayed in appropriate places about the vessel – all seafarers should understand and be able to follow the procedures shown on the notices.

5.3.3. Laundry and wet clothing

5.3.3.1. Care should be taken when drying items of clothing. Clothing should not be hung directly on or close to heaters and should never be dried in the engine-room.

5.3.4. Spontaneous combustion

5.3.4.1. Waste, rags, and other rubbish as well as clothes soaked with paint, oil, thinners, etc., are dangerous if left lying around as they may spontaneously combust. All waste should be stored in proper dustbins until it can be safely disposed of.

5.3.5. Galleys

5.3.5.1. Galleys present particular fire hazards and the means to smother fat or cooking oil fires, such as a fire blanket and appropriate fire extinguisher, should be readily available (see also Chapter 22). Water shall never be used in attempts to fight fires involving hot oil in cooking areas.

5.4. Working clothes and personal protective equipment[1]

5.4.1. General

5.4.1.1. Working clothes should be close fitting with no loose flaps and should be appropriate for the work being carried out.

5.4.1.2. Suitable safety footwear should be worn at all times.

5.4.1.3. Shipowners should ensure that seafarers are supplied with suitable personal protective equipment, particularly when engaged in work involving a particular hazard which can be reduced by the provision of personal protective equipment.

5.4.1.4. Seafarers should be reminded that the provision of personal protective equipment does not mean that they can lower their

---

[1] Reference may also be made to Chapter 27 of *Safety and Health in Dock Work: An ILO Code of practice* (2nd revised ed., 1977).

own safety standards and that such equipment does not eliminate hazards but gives only limited protection in the case of accidents.

5.4.1.5. Personal protective equipment should be of a type and standard as approved by the appropriate authority. A wide variety of equipment is available and it is essential that no items are ordered, or received on board, unless they are suitable for the task for which they are required.

5.4.1.6. The manufacturer's instructions should be kept safe with the relevant equipment and consulted for use and maintenance purposes.

5.4.1.7. The effectiveness of personal protective equipment depends not only on its design but on its maintenance in good condition. Such items should be inspected at regular intervals.

5.4.1.8. All seafarers should be trained in the use of personal protective equipment and advised of its limitations. Persons using such items should check them each time before use.

5.4.1.9. Special personal protective equipment should be provided and worn by seafarers who may be exposed to particular corrosive or contaminating substances.

5.4.1.10. Clothing worn in galleys and machinery spaces where there is a risk of burning or scalding should adequately cover the body to minimize the hazard and should be of a material of low flammability, such as cotton.

5.4.2. Head protection

5.4.2.1. Helmets may be designed for different purposes. A helmet designed to provide protection from objects falling from above may not be suitable for protecting seafarers from chemical splashes. Thus, it may be necessary to carry different types of helmets on particular ships.

5.4.2.2. In general, the shell of a helmet should be of one-piece construction, with an adjustable cradle inside to support the helmet on the wearer's head and, where appropriate, a chin-strap to prevent the helmet from falling off.

5.4.2.3. The cradle and chin-strap should be properly adjusted as soon as the helmet is put on to ensure a snug fit.

5.4.3. Hearing protection

5.4.3.1. Seafarers who by the nature of their duties are exposed to high levels of noise, such as those working in machinery spaces, should be provided with and should wear ear protectors.

5.4.3.2. Various types of hearing protectors are available for shipboard use, including ear plugs and ear muffs, each of which may be of different design standards. Protectors should be of a type recommended as suitable for the particular circumstances and climatic conditions.

5.4.3.3. In general, ear muffs give the most effective protection.

5.4.3.4. Hearing protectors should be made available at the entrance to the machinery space.

5.4.4. Face and eye protection

5.4.4.1. Face and eye protectors are available in a wide variety of designs. Careful consideration should be given to the characteristics of the respective hazard to ensure the selection of the appropriate protector.

5.4.4.2. Ordinary prescription (corrective) spectacles, unless manufactured to a safety standard, do not afford protection. Certain box-type goggles are designed so that they can be worn over ordinary spectacles.

5.4.5. Respiratory protective equipment[1]

5.4.5.1. Appropriate respiratory protective equipment should be provided for work in conditions where there is a risk of oxygen deficiency or exposure to poisonous, dangerous or irritating fumes, dust, or gases.

5.4.5.2. The selection of correct equipment is essential. Since there is a wide variety of equipment available for shipboard use, advice should be sought on the appropriate equipment for use on particular ships and for particular purposes.

5.4.5.3. Seafarers should be trained in the use and care of equipment.

5.4.5.4. The face-piece incorporated in respirators and breathing apparatus must be fitted correctly to prevent leakage. The wearing of spectacles, unless adequately designed for the purpose, or beards and whiskers are likely to interfere with the face seal.

5.4.6. Hand and foot protection

5.4.6.1. Gloves should give protection from the particular hazard of the work being carried out and must be appropriate to that type of work. For example, leather gloves are generally better for handling rough or sharp objects, heat-resistant gloves for handling hot objects, and rubber, synthetic or PVC gloves for handling acids, alkalis, various types of oils, solvents and chemicals.

5.4.6.2. All seafarers at work should wear appropriate safety footwear. Shoes and boots should have firm, slip-resistant soles and

---

[1] See also Chapter 10: "Entering and working in enclosed or confined spaces".

reinforced toecaps. Sandals and similar footwear should not be worn when working.

5.4.7. Protection from falls

5.4.7.1. Seafarers working aloft, over the side, or where there is a risk of falling, should wear a safety harness attached to a lifeline (see also Chapter 15).

5.5. Signs, notices and colour codes

5.5.1. Signs and symbols are a very effective method for warning against hazards and for presenting information in a non-linguistic form. Safety signs and notices should conform in shape and colour to the requirements of the competent authority.

5.5.2. The contents of portable fire extinguishers should be indicated by a colour code in compliance with the requirements of the competent authority. Each fire extinguisher should have a label affixed to it providing instructions for its use.

5.5.3. Various standards exist for the colour coding of electrical wiring cores and care should always be taken to ensure that personnel are aware of the meaning of the core colours on board each ship. If a replacement is required, it should be in accordance with the coding system.

5.5.4. Gas cylinders should be clearly marked with the name of the gas, its chemical formula or symbol and the body should be coloured according to its contents. A colour coding card should be provided.

5.5.5. Pipelines should be marked with a colour coding system which indicates their contents. Replacement pipe should be marked consistently with the colour coding system.

5.5.6. Packages containing dangerous goods should be appropriately marked (see also Chapter 7).

6. Shipboard emergencies and emergency equipment

6.1. General provisions

6.1.1. National and international requirements governing equipment, musters, drills and training should be strictly complied with.[1]

6.1.2. Shipboard emergency training schemes should take account of the *IMO/ILO Document for guidance: An international maritime training guide* (1985 or later edition).[2]

6.1.3. Seafarers should be informed of the location to which they must go on hearing the emergency signal and of their duties when they arrive at that station. The location should be well marked.

6.1.4. The master should ensure that a muster list is compiled and kept up to date and that copies are displayed in conspicuous places throughout the ship. The muster list should contain details of the general alarm signal and other emergency signals and the action to be taken when such signals are activated. The means by which the order to abandon ship is given should also be included. The muster list should indicate the individual duties of all personnel on board and all crew members should be given written details of their own duties.

6.1.5. All seafarers concerned should muster at a drill wearing the appropriate clothing.

---

[1] In particular, SOLAS, 1974, Chapter III, as amended.
[2] In particular sections 10, 11 and 12.

6.1.6. The purpose of drills is to familiarize personnel with their respective duties and to ensure that they can carry out those duties in an appropriate manner. Each crew member should participate in drills in accordance with national and international requirements.[1]

6.1.7. The timing of drills should be varied to ensure that seafarers who because of their duties have not taken part in a particular drill may participate in the next drill. Seafarers should receive training as soon as possible, if possible before joining the ship, to ensure that there is no period of time when the seafarer is incapable of carrying out safety-related responsibilities.

6.1.8. Drills often involve the whole crew but it might be preferable to confine certain drills to crew members with specific tasks.

6.1.9. Although drills are an essential part of emergency training, a training scheme should consist of more than just drills. Information should be given to the entire crew on subjects such as "cold water survival"[2] and instruction provided to certain crew members on the use of particular items of equipment.

6.2. Fire-fighting equipment, drills and training

6.2.1. (1) Fire protection devices, fire-extinguishing appliances, breathing apparatus and other safety equipment should be provided in accordance with the regulations applicable to the ship and to the satisfaction of the appropriate authority.

(2) This equipment should be maintained in good order in accordance with the manufacturer's instructions and kept available for use at all times.

---

[1] SOLAS, 1974, Chapter III, as amended.

[2] For example, a copy of the IMO *Pocket guide to cold water survival*, could be provided to each seafarer.

6.2.2. Seafarers should not interfere with or discharge any fire extinguisher without due cause, and should report any faults or cases of accidental discharge to a responsible officer.

6.2.3. Immediately after joining, when appropriate, seafarers should familiarize themselves with the location of the fire-fighting appliances on board, the operation of such appliances and their effectiveness on different types of fires. This knowledge should be verified by a responsible officer. (For guidance with respect to passenger vessels, see Chapter 24.)

6.2.4. Appropriate crew members on board should be trained in the use of the following fire-fighting appliances:

(a) all types of portable fire extinguishers carried on board;

(b) self-contained breathing apparatus;

(c) hoses with jet and spray nozzles;

(d) any fixed fire-fighting system such as foam or carbon dioxide;

(e) fire blankets; and

(f) firemen's outfits.

6.2.5. When possible, fire drills should be held in port as well as at sea.

6.2.6. Although many fires occur in port, it may prove difficult to arrange a drill with the local fire authorities. This problem can be partly resolved by instructing the crew on the nature of shore requirements using the contents of the fire wallet (which should be positioned by the access arrangements and which contains information required by shore fire authorities who are required to fight a fire on board ship).[1]

---

[1] SOLAS, 1974, Chapter II, as amended.

6.2.7. It is important that the symbols used on a ship's fire control plan are understood by shore fire personnel. Graphic symbols should be used as much as possible.[1]

6.2.8. Efficient fire-fighting requires the full cooperation of personnel in all departments of the vessel.

6.2.9. For the purpose of a fire drill an outbreak of fire should be assumed to have occurred in some part of the ship, the alarm should be activated and the requisite actions taken be in accordance with the ship's safety and health policy.

6.2.10. The type and position of the fire scenario should be varied in a well-conceived sequence which covers most parts of the ship and all types of fire-fighting. Locations could include:

(a)   holds, tanks and other spaces such as forepeak stores and paint lockers;

(b)   engine or boiler rooms;

(c)   accommodation spaces such as cabins and laundry rooms; and

(d)   galleys.

6.2.11. Fire drills should be as realistic as circumstances permit. When possible, local fire-fighting equipment, such as extinguishers, should be activated and the visibility of self-contained breathing apparatus masks should be reduced to give the impression of operating within a smoke-filled atmosphere.

6.2.12. The fixed water fire-fighting system should be used and engine room staff should ensure that the fire pumps are operated and that full water pressure is on the fire mains. The emergency fire pump should also be used for fire drills and personnel should be trained in the operation of other fixed systems such as foam and carbon dioxide.

---

[1] These are the symbols recommended in Resolution A.654(16) (1989), of the IMO.

6.2.13. All equipment activated during fire drills should be immediately replaced with fully loaded appliances.

6.2.14. Seafarers should be exercised in the closing of openings and the closing down of ventilation systems.

6.2.15. A fire drill can be held as the first stage of an abandon ship drill.

6.3. Abandon ship drills and training[1]

6.3.1. Each abandon ship drill should include:

(a) summoning personnel to muster stations by the general alarm and ensuring that they are made aware of the order to abandon ship. A check should be carried out to ensure that all personnel are at muster stations;

(b) reporting to stations and preparing for the duties described in the muster list;

(c) checking that personnel are suitably dressed to minimize cold shock if direct entry into the sea is necessary;

(d) checking that life-jackets are correctly donned;

(e) where possible, lowering of at least one lifeboat after any necessary preparation for launching;

(f) starting and operating the lifeboat engine;

(g) where fitted, operating of davits for launching liferafts; and

(h) divers in saturation are not able to take advantage of conventional lifeboats in an emergency. The IMO guidelines should be

---

[1] Abandoning ship and other life-saving drills should be carried out in accordance with national requirements, which should be at least equivalent to those of Chapter III of the Annex to SOLAS (1974), as amended.

followed for these divers. Compliance with the IMO guidelines will satisfy Chapter 3 of the Code of Safety for Diving Systems, IMO Resolution A.831(19).

6.3.2. Inflatable liferafts must be sent for regular servicing. If possible, abandon ship drills should be held when a liferaft is due to be sent for servicing. Invaluable experience can be obtained by actually inflating a liferaft in the water and exercising the crew in liferaft boarding techniques.

6.3.3. Each lifeboat should be launched and manoeuvred in the water at least once every three months. If possible, lowering or hoisting a boat with crew on board should be avoided.

6.3.4. When turning out davits or bringing boats or rafts inboard under power, seafarers should always keep clear of any moving parts.

6.3.5. The crank handle of a lifeboat winch is designed not to rotate except for manual hoisting action. Nevertheless, such handles should be removed from the winch as soon as manual hoisting is stopped. If, however, for some reason the handle cannot be removed and there is a chance of the handle rotating under the action of gravity or electricity, seafarers should keep well away from the handle although it may seem stationery.

6.3.6. (1) Seafarers in an open lifeboat being lowered should remain seated, holding their lines and should have their hands inside the gunwale to avoid them being crushed against the ship's side.

(2) Seafarers should keep their fingers clear of the long-link when unhooking or securing blocks on to lifting hooks while the boat is in the water.

6.3.7. Before craft in gravity davits are recovered by power, the operation of the limit switches and similar devices should be checked.

6.3.8. Free-fall lifeboats should at all times be boarded in an orderly manner. Seafarers should immediately secure themselves into the seat with the restraining harness and carry out the instructions of the responsible officer.

6.4. Helicopter operations[1]

6.4.1. A sufficient number of crew members should be trained in helicopter operations.

6.4.2. A safety check-list should be used as the basis for preparing for all ship/helicopter operations. The check-list should include such typical provisions as:

(a) all loose objects should be secured or removed;

(b) all aerials should be lowered;

(c) fire hoses should be ready, pumps running and adequate water pressure provided on deck;

(d) foam hoses, monitors and portable foam equipment should be ready;

(e) additional equipment, such as wire cutters and crowbars, should be ready;

(f) railings should be lowered where appropriate; and

(g) flag pennants or wind socks should be used to indicate wind direction.

---

[1] The safety of the helicopter crew, as well as of seafarers, must be considered. Reference should be made, for example, to the *Guide to helicopter/ship operations* (3rd edition, 1989 or later edition), published by the International Chamber of Shipping.

6.4.3. A contingency plan should be devised to minimize the effect of a helicopter crashing onto the ship and seafarers should be trained in the operation of the plan. The plan should provide for:

(a) foam equipment operators, at least two wearing firemen's outfits, standing by;

(b) rescue party, with at least two members wearing firemen's outfits, standing by;

(c) man overboard rescue boat ready for immediate lowering; and

(d) hook handlers equipped with suitable gloves and rubber boots.

6.4.4. The crew should be trained in procedures for evacuation by helicopter.

6.4.5. A winching area to be used for helicopter operations should be established. The area should include an inner clear zone, which is a totally clear plated area having a minimum diameter of 5 m, and an outer manoeuvring zone, which is a circular area at least 30 m in diameter in which the height of all obstacles must not be more than 3 m.

6.5. Man overboard and rescue at sea

6.5.1. Each ship should have a contingency plan in the event that someone falls overboard. The plan should take into account the particular characteristics of the ship, the life-saving equipment available and the size of the crew. For example, a typical drill could be the action taken if the bridge watchkeeping officer observes someone falling from the main deck into the sea. This would include:

(a) executing a Williamson turn or other ship's turn as appropriate;

(b) dropping the bridge wing quick-release lifebuoy;

(c) sounding the general or emergency squad alarm;

(d) announcing the type of emergency over the public address system so that the rescue boat can be prepared;

(e) assigning a person to the wheel and posting lookouts;

(f) radar "marking" of the man overboard position;

(g) initiating any communication such as a "Pan Pan Pan" message; and

(h) positioning the ship to make a lee and launching the rescue boat.

6.5.2. It should be remembered that it may take the master a few minutes to reach the bridge before he can take over the operation and that some decisions need to be taken before he reaches the bridge.

6.5.3. The procedure on how to pull a person from the sea into a boat should, when possible, be practised during periods when a ship is at anchor.

6.5.4. Should a search be necessary the procedures described in the *Merchant ship search and rescue manual* (MERSAR), published by the IMO, should be adopted, especially if the search is carried out with other ships.

6.6. Other drills

6.6.1. Emergency training should not be limited to abandoning ship, fire-fighting and man-overboard drills. Seafarers should undergo continuous and refresher training in any emergency situations likely to occur aboard the ship.

6.6.2. Drills in the rescue of seafarers in confined spaces are critical. Seafarers should be thoroughly trained in the procedures described in Chapter 10.

6.6.3. Seafarers should receive first-aid training prior to board-ing the ship. Special training should be provided for particular types of cargoes and operations. Refresher training should be given on a regular basis. Posters, pamphlets and other means of reminding sea-farers of first-aid procedures should be posted or otherwise made available throughout the ship.

7. Carriage of dangerous goods

7.1. General provisions[1]

7.1.1. The provisions of the International Maritime Dangerous Goods (IMDG) Code and any national laws and regulations are to be observed.

7.1.2. No dangerous goods should be loaded if not accompanied by appropriate documentation. The documentation should state the correct technical name of the goods (the manufacturer's trade name alone is not sufficient) and the United Nations number so that the relevant information can be found in the IMO codes. The goods are to be correctly described using the IMDG classification system.

7.1.3. Dangerous substances should be loaded or unloaded only under the supervision of a responsible officer.

7.1.4. Goods should not be loaded if the packaging does not comply with IMDG standards.

7.1.5. Packages are to be durably marked with the correct technical name and the contents are to be identified by the IMDG classification and labelling system.

7.1.6. No containers or road vehicles containing dangerous goods should be loaded without the provision of a container-packing certificate or vehicle-packing certificate where required.

7.1.7. Seafarers should be advised beforehand of the dangerous nature of the goods and of any necessary precautions to be ob-

---

[1] The *International Maritime Dangerous Goods Code* should be consulted before any known or suspected dangerous goods are loaded.

served. Seafarers required to handle consignments containing dangerous substances are to be given adequate information on the nature of the substances and any special precautions which are to be taken. If accidental exposure to dangerous substances occurs, the IMO's Medical First Aid Guide for Use in Accidents Involving Dangerous Goods (MFAG) should be consulted.[1]

7.1.8. The shipper should be responsible for informing the shipowner of any special hazard, and should be required to forward instructions on the dangers and the medical treatment of accidental spillage or poisoning and, if necessary, should supply any special drugs required.[2]

7.1.9. Dangerous goods which are liable to interact dangerously are to be effectively segregated from one another in accordance with the IMDG Code.

7.1.10. Explosives and other hazardous goods should be carried only in strict accordance with the IMDG Code requirements.

7.1.11. Each ship carrying hazardous goods should have a detailed stowage plan which shows the location of all hazardous goods on board and which identifies the goods by class. A copy should be available before departure for the respective shore authorities and another copy should be kept on the vessel's bridge. The stowage plan, or at least the location of dangerous cargoes, should be made available to the safety and health committee before the ship is loaded.

---

[1] The ILO *Code of Practice on Safety and Health in Dock Work* also provides that port workers should be advised on the handling of dangerous goods.

[2] For additional information, the IMDG Code and the IMO/WHO/ILO *Medical first aid guide for use in accidents involving dangerous goods* (MFAG), published by the IMO, should be consulted.

7.1.12. Substances which are liable to spontaneous heating or combustion should only be carried under the provision of the relevant codes.[1, 2, 3]

7.1.13. Correct measures should be taken promptly to render harmless any spillage of dangerous substances. Particular attention may be necessary if such substances are transported in refrigerated compartments where spillage may be absorbed by insulating material.

7.1.14. On the discovery of leakage of dangerous goods or of damaged packing, work must cease immediately and should be resumed only after advice and instruction on the necessary safety precautions to be taken. Otherwise, work should be resumed (depending on the degree of danger) only after seafarers have put on protective clothing appropriate to the nature of the goods to be handled.

7.1.15. In the event of leakage or spillage involving dangerous gas or fumes, the use of a gas detector is advised before a space is declared to be safe (see Chapter 10). Gas masks should only be used for purposes of escape. The place where the leakage has occurred should be treated immediately with an appropriate neutralizing substance.

7.2. Special precautions

7.2.1. (1) The IMDG Code contains many provisions for ensuring the safe handling and carriage of dangerous goods, including requirements for electrical equipment and wiring, fire-fighting equip-

---

[1] IMDG Code.

[2] Code of Safe Practice for Solid Bulk Cargoes (BC Code).

[3] Additional precautions are to be taken for specific types of cargoes, such as plutonium. The appropriate codes and resolutions of the IMO are to be complied with in such circumstances.

ment, ventilation, smoking, repair work, provision and availability of special equipment, etc., and should be referred to before handling dangerous goods.

(2) Before the loading of particular consignments, officers should check the individual entries in the codes to ensure that the vessel has the appropriate fire-fighting equipment and extinguishing agent should a fire occur.

(3) Since some substances which catch fire may emit poisonous fumes, protective clothing and sets of self-contained breathing apparatus should be readily available.

(4) Packages should be stowed in a location which ensures protection from accidental damage or heating.

(5) Dangerous goods are to be segregated from substances which are liable to start or to spread fires.

(6) Dangerous goods should be stowed away from living quarters.

(7) It may be necessary to ensure accessibility of dangerous goods so that packages in the vicinity of a fire may be protected or moved to safety.

(8) Before loading commence, any fire detection system should be tested.

(9) During loading, suitable fire-fighting appliances should be ready for use and all unauthorized personnel should be cleared of the area.

(10) A responsible person should be present when dangerous goods are being loaded and all packages should be tallied.

7.2.2. On any vessel liable to transport dangerous substances where conditions of operation do not allow advance notice of the nature of the dangerous substances being transported, there should be carried on board medical supplies including at least the antidotes listed in the IMDG Code. However, on a regular trade, the antidotes might be limited to those which have to be administered in cases of extreme emergency within a period of time not exceeding the normal duration of the crossing.

7.3. Additional sources of information

7.3.1. The IMO *Code of Safe Practice for Solid Bulk Cargoes* (BC Code), provides guidance in the safe stowage and shipment of solid bulk cargoes, excluding grain. It includes general advice on the procedures to be followed whenever bulk cargoes are to be shipped, a description of the hazards associated with certain materials and lists of typical material currently shipped in bulk.

7.3.2. The (IMO) Code of Safe Practice for Solid Bulk Cargoes, Appendix B is to be followed where certain solid dangerous substances are shipped in bulk. Additional advice can be found in Chapter 24.

7.3.3. The IMO publication *Emergency procedures for ships carrying dangerous goods* (EmS) gives information on the action to be taken in the event of an incident involving certain dangerous goods. The goods included in the EmS are classified according to the IMDG Code and are grouped so that goods requiring the same or similar emergency action appear on one emergency schedule. Each emergency schedule is divided into five sections:

(a) group title with the emergency schedule number;

(b) special equipment required;

(c) emergency procedures;

(d) emergency action;

(e) first aid.

The appropriate schedules should be consulted before goods are loaded to ascertain that the vessel has the correct equipment to deal with any incidents which might occur.

7.3.4. Pesticides used on board ship may be classed as dangerous goods; information on various aspects of pest control can be found in the IMO *Recommendations on the safe use of pesticides in ships*.

8. Safe access to ship[1]

8.1. Means of access to ship

8.1.1. There should be a safe means of access between any ship and any quay, pontoon or similar structure or another ship alongside which the ship is secured.

8.1.2. Seafarers should be provided with adequate information on how to make their way safely to and from the ship through the marine terminal or shoreside cargo handling area.[2]

8.1.3. In some modern ports access equipment and information on safe means of access are provided by the port authorities. However, the master should ensure, as far as possible, that the equipment meets the required safety standards.

8.1.4. Seafarers should not use a means of access which is unsafe. They should also use means of access with care, e.g. they should make several trips or use a stores crane when carrying personal gear, stores or ship's equipment rather than attempting to carry too much at once.

8.1.5. All access arrangements should be supervised at all times, either by seafarers or by shore personnel, particularly in ports which have large tidal ranges.[3]

---

[1] The ILO *Code of Practice on Safety and Health in Dock Work* (revised, 1977) and the ILO *Guide to safety and health in dock work* (revised, 1988) contain more detailed information on means of access to vessels.

[2] The duty to ensure the safety of seafarers in port areas is stressed in the Seafarers' Welfare at Sea and in Port Recommendation, 1987 (No. 173) (Paragraphs 3 and 19).

[3] Besides contributing to the protection of seafarers against accidents, such surveillance also enhances security against unauthorized persons, including criminals, from boarding the vessel.

8.1.6. Access should generally be by an accommodation ladder or gangway which is appropriate to the deck layout, size, shape and maximum freeboard of the ship.

8.1.7. Any access equipment should be of good construction, sound material, adequate strength, free from obvious defect, properly maintained and inspected at frequent intervals. It should not be painted or treated to conceal cracks or defects.

8.1.8. Access equipment should be placed in position promptly after the ship has been secured and remain in position while the ship is secured.

8.1.9. A lifebuoy with a self-activating light and a separate safety line or some similar device should be provided at the point of access aboard the ship.

8.1.10. All access equipment and the approaches to such equipment should be properly illuminated.

8.1.11. Seafarers should use only the appropriate equipment for ship access.

8.1.12. As far as is practicable, access equipment should be kept free of any snow, ice, grease or other substance likely to cause a slip or fall.

8.1.13. Any gap between the dockside and the ship, whereby a person on the ship's means of access might fall into the water, should be protected by a safety net, of suitable size, mesh and construction, secured to the ship and dockside, as appropriate.

8.1.14. The means of access and its immediate approaches should be kept free from obstruction and, as far as practicable, kept clear of any substance likely to cause a slip or fall.

8.1.15. The means of access should be sited so that no suspended load passes over it.

8.1.16. Gangways and accommodation ladders should be clearly marked with the maximum permitted angle of use and maximum safe loading in both number of persons and total weight. Under no circumstances should this limit be exceeded.

8.1.17. Further guidance concerning access to vehicle ferries or roll-on/roll-off vessels may be found in Chapter 24.

8.2. Ship's accommodation ladders and gangways

8.2.1. (1) Any accommodation ladder or gangways should be:

(a) at least 55 cm in width; and
(b) provided with stanchions and taut rails, chains or fencing on both sides.

(2) Stanchions should not be more than 3 m apart, and properly secured to avoid inadvertent displacement.

(3) Fencing should be at least 1m high, with an intermediate rail or chain at a height of about 50 cm.

(4) The accommodation ladder or gangway should be so constructed that ordinary changes in the ship's draught or height above the quay can be easily accommodated.

(5) Where practicable, accommodation ladders should have a swivel top platform, slip-resistant treads and wheels or rollers at the bottom.

(6) Any necessary adjustment should not tilt the treads or steps to such an extent that they cease to offer a firm foothold.

(7) Duckboards should be fitted to provide a secure foothold at small angles of inclination.

8.2.2. (1) The gap between the top of the gangway or ladder and the ship should be protected on each side by handrails, taut chains or other suitable means, with intermediate chains at a height to match the handrails and intermediate protection of the gangway.

(2) If the upper end rests on or is flush with the top of a rail or bulwark, substantial and properly secured steps fitted with an adequate handrail should be provided to ensure safe passage to and from the gangway.

8.2.3. Where practicable, accommodation ladders should not be used at a greater angle to the horizontal than 55 degrees.

8.2.4. If the gangway rests on rollers or wheels, it should be fitted or protected in such a way as to prevent the user's feet from being caught and it should be placed in a position which does not restrict the free movement of the rollers or wheels.

8.2.5. A gangway should never be permitted to drop between the shore and the ship in such a way that it may be crushed or damaged.

8.2.6. (1) Special care should be taken during maintenance to detect any cracking, rusting or corrosion in gangways, ladders and metal fittings.

(2) Any defects posing a hazard should be made good before further use.

8.3. Portable ladders

8.3.1. A portable ladder should not be used for access to a vessel unless a safer means of access is not reasonably practical.

8.3.2. Portable ladders should be of good construction, adequate strength and properly maintained.

.8.3.3. When a ladder is in use:

(a) the top should rise at least 1 m above the landing place;

(b) each upright should rest properly on a firm and level footing; and

(c) it should be properly secured against slipping, falling or sideways shifting.

8.3.4. The ladder should be used at an angle of between 60 and 75 degrees from the horizontal.

8.4. Pilot ladders

8.4.1. The requirements for pilot ladders and mechanical pilot hoists found in SOLAS, 1974, Chapter V, Regulation 17, are to be observed.

8.5. Transport of persons by water

8.5.1. When persons have to be transported to or from a ship by water, suitable and proper measures should be taken to provide for their safe passage. The boats used should be of suitable construction, properly equipped and maintained and suitably crewed. Embarkation and disembarkation should take place only at suitable and safe landing places.

9. Safe movement about the ship

9.1. General provisions

9.1.1. Seafarers should move about the ship bearing in mind the possibility of an unusual lurch or heavy roll by the ship while at sea.

9.1.2. Permanent fittings which cause obstruction and which may be dangerous to vehicles, lifting appliances or persons should be made conspicuous by means of colouring, marking or lighting.

9.1.3. (1) Any deck obstructions and head-height obstructions that are a hazard should be painted a bright, conspicuous colour.

(2) Where necessary, warning notices should be posted. Graphic symbols should be utilized where possible.

(3) Head-height obstructions should be padded.

9.1.4. The stowage of deck cargoes should take account of the requirements for safe access to crew quarters, for crew working the ship, for boarding of pilots, and access to safety equipment.

9.2. Passageways and walkways

9.2.1. All passageways, walkways, stairs and all deck surfaces used for transit should be properly maintained and kept free from materials or substances liable to cause slips or falls.

9.2.2. Transit areas should, where practicable, be provided with a surface which is slip resistant in dry as well as in wet conditions.

9.2.3. Walkways on deck should be delineated by painted lines or otherwise and indicated by signs.

9.2.4. Any gear or equipment stowed to the side of a passageway or walkway should be securely fixed or lashed against the movement of the ship when at sea.

9.2.5. When rough weather is expected, lifelines should be rigged securely across open decks.

9.3. Watertight doors

9.3.1. All seafarers who may have to use watertight doors should be instructed in their safe use.

9.3.2. Power-operated watertight doors can be closed from the bridge and particular care should be taken when using such doors. If opened locally under these circumstances a door will reclose automatically and crush anyone in its path as soon as local control has been released. Both hands are usually required to operate the local controls, and for this reason no person should alone attempt to carry any load through such doors. The bridge should be notified whenever such doors are opened and immediately after they are closed.

9.3.3. Notices clearly stating the method of operating the local controls of watertight doors should be prominently displayed on both sides of the doors.

9.3.4. (1) No attempt should be made to pass through a watertight door when it is closing or when the warning alarm is sounding.

(2) Whenever a watertight door is energized, and under remote control, transit is not allowed. If necessary to leave the area confined by such doors, emergency exits shall be used. A warning to that effect shall be displayed at the local operating point.

9.4. Lighting

9.4.1. Areas of the ship used for loading or unloading, other work processes or transit should be adequately and appropriately illuminated.

9.4.2. Lighting should be reasonably constant and arranged to minimize glare, dazzle and the formation of deep shadows and sharp contrasts between one area and another.

9.4.3. Broken or defective lights should be reported immediately and repaired as soon as practicable.

9.4.4. It should be prohibited to enter unlighted or inadequately lighted places on the ship without safe portable lights.

9.4.5. Lights, both fixed and portable, should be checked to ensure proper operation and safe rigging prior to use. No operation should be permitted to commence or continue if lighting is insufficient.

9.5. Protection around cargo hatches and other deck openings

9.5.1. Every cargo hatchway should be protected by means of a coaming or fencing to a height of at least 1 m above the deck.

9.5.2. Hatch covers, pontoons and beams that have been removed should be placed so as to leave a safe walkway from rail to hatch coaming and fore and aft.

9.5.3. Access within cargo spaces and holds should be kept clear.

9.5.4. Mechanically, hydraulically and electrically powered hatch covers should be opened and closed only by designated members of the ship's crew or other authorized persons. The hatches should only be operated after ensuring it is clear to do so.

9.5.5. Any openings through which a person might fall should be fitted with secure guards or fencing of adequate design and construction.

9.5.6. Guard-rails or fencing should consist of an upper rail at a height of 1 m and an intermediate rail at a height of 50 cm. The rails may consist of taut wire or taut chain.

9.6. Access to holds and other spaces

9.6.1. Safe access should be provided into each hold or space below deck, in accordance with SOLAS requirements, as amended.

9.6.2. Rope ladders should not be used to access holds.

9.6.3. (1) All ladders and access arrangements should be inspected at frequent intervals by a competent officer, especially before and after working cargo in the space in question.

(2) When any ladders, handgrips, footholds or cleats are found to be unsafe, access should be locked or blocked off and warning notices prohibiting access should be posted at every approach until repairs have been carried out.

9.6.4. (1) The competent officer should ensure that any defects are corrected as soon as practicable.

(2) Any welding or replacement of rungs, ladders or cleats should be inspected and tested by a competent officer before use to ensure that it has been properly carried out.

9.7. Drainage

9.7.1. Drains and scuppers should be regularly inspected and properly maintained to ensure that they do not become blocked.

10. Entering and working in enclosed or confined spaces

10.1. General provisions

10.1.1. All enclosed or confined spaces should be considered unsafe for entry until proven otherwise.

10.1.2. If there is an unexpected reduction in or loss of ventilation, in spaces which are usually ventilated by whatever means, then those spaces should also be considered as dangerous.

10.1.3. Any enclosed or confined space may have an atmosphere deficient in oxygen, and/or contain flammable or toxic fumes, gases or vapours, thus presenting a major risk to health or life for anyone entering it. Areas in which an unsafe atmosphere is present or can arise include cargo holds, double bottoms, cargo tanks, pump rooms, compressor rooms, fuel tanks, ballast tanks, cofferdams, void spaces, duct keels, inter-barrier spaces, sewage tanks, cable trunks, pipe trunks, pressure vessels, battery lockers, chain lockers, inert gas plant scrubber and blower spaces and the storage rooms for CO_2, halons and other media used for fire extinguishing or inerting.

10.1.4. Such enclosed or confined spaces should not be entered except upon the explicit instruction of the master or the responsible officer. If a deficiency of oxygen or the presence of toxic gases, vapours or fumes is suspected in any space, then that space should be considered dangerous.

10.1.5. The crew should be drilled periodically in confined spaces rescue and medical first aid.

10.2. Precautions on entering dangerous spaces

10.2.1. Before a space is entered, the following precautions should be taken, as appropriate, to make it safe for entry without the need for breathing apparatus, and to ensure that it remains safe whilst seafarers are inside:

(a) a competent person should make an assessment of the space and a responsible officer should be appointed to take charge of the operation;

(b) the potential hazards should be identified;

(c) the space should be prepared and secured for entry;

(d) the atmosphere should be tested;

(e) a "permit-to-work" system should be used (see Chapter 4);

(f) entry procedures should be established and followed;

(g) continuous ventilation should be maintained throughout.

10.2.2. Additional precautions, including the use of breathing apparatus,[1] should be taken where 10.2.1 has been followed and an unsafe atmosphere has been established. (See section 10.9.)

10.2.3. A seafarer should not enter a dangerous space to attempt a rescue without first having called for assistance and then having donned a breathing apparatus. Even then entry should not be made until assistance arrives (see sections 10.9 and 10.10).

10.3. Duties and responsibilities of a competent person and of a responsible officer

10.3.1. The designated competent person should be capable of making an informed assessment of the likelihood of a dangerous

---

[1] SOLAS (1974), Chapter II, as amended.

atmosphere being present or arising subsequently in a space. The competent person should have sufficient theoretical knowledge and practical experience of the hazards that might be met in order to be able to assess whether precautions are necessary. The assessment should include any potential hazards which might be met, and should take into account any dangers from neighbouring or unconnected spaces, as well as the work needing to be done in the space itself.

10.3.2. A responsible officer should be designated to take charge of every operation where entry into a potentially dangerous space is necessary. This officer may be the same person as the competent person.

10.3.3. The responsible officer must decide on the basis of the competent person's assessment the procedures which must be followed for entry into the space. These will depend on whether the assessment shows:

(a) no risk is envisaged to the life or health of a person entering the space;

(b) no immediate risk to life or health but that a risk could arise during the course of work in the space (the precautions in section 10.5 should then be followed);

(c) an immediate risk to life or health (the precautions in section 10.9 should then be followed).

10.3.4. If no risk to life or health is envisaged, and it is considered that conditions in the space will not change, then entry may be made. The space should be monitored as long as anyone is inside.

10.4. Preparing and securing the space for entry

10.4.1. Care should be taken to avoid the effects of a possible release of pressure or vapour when opening the entrance to the space.

10.4.2. The space should be isolated and secured against the escape of dangerous substances by blanking off pipelines or other openings or by closing valves. Valves should then be tied, or some other method employed to show that they must not be opened.

10.4.3. The space should be cleaned or washed if necessary, to remove as much as possible of the sludge or other deposit liable to give off dangerous fumes. Special precautions may be necessary (see section 10.9).

10.4.4. The space should be thoroughly ventilated by natural or mechanical means, to ensure that all harmful gases are removed and no pockets of oxygen-deficient atmosphere remain. Compressed oxygen should not be used to ventilate any space.

10.4.5. Officers on watch, or persons in charge, on the bridge, on the deck, in the engine-room, or the cargo control room should be informed as necessary of any space to be entered so that, for example, fans are not stopped, equipment not started or valves not opened by remote control.

10.4.6. Appropriate warning notices should be placed on the relevant controls or equipment.

10.4.7. Where necessary, pumping operations or cargo movements should be suspended when entry is being made into a dangerous space.

10.5. Testing the atmosphere of confined and enclosed spaces

10.5.1. Only persons trained in the use of the equipment should test the atmosphere of a space.

10.5.2. Equipment should be properly calibrated before use.

10.5.3. Testing of the atmosphere should be carried out before entry and at regular intervals thereafter.

10.5.4. Testing of the atmosphere before entry should be made by remote means. If not possible, the competent person should ensure that all attempts have been made to reduce the danger posed by the atmosphere and only then should entry be made with the additional precautions set out in section 10.9.

10.5.5. Testing of the atmosphere should be carried out on different levels, where appropriate.

10.5.6. Personal monitoring equipment designed purely to provide a warning against oxygen deficiency and hydrocarbon concentrations should not be used as a means of determining whether a dangerous space is safe to enter.

10.6. Use of a permit-to-work system

10.6.1. A "permit-to-work" system should be used (see Chapter 4). Entry into a space should be planned in advance and if unforeseen problems or hazards arise during the operation, then work should be stopped and the space evacuated immediately. Permits to work should be withdrawn, and the situation reassessed. Permits to work should be revised as appropriate after the reassessment.

10.6.2. Everyone should leave the space on expiry of a "permit to work", and the entrance should be closed or otherwise secured to prevent re-entry, or declared safe for normal entry when it is no longer dangerous.

10.7. Procedures and arrangements before entry

10.7.1. Access to and lighting within the space should be adequate.

10.7.2. No sources of ignition should be taken or put into the space unless the master or responsible officer is satisfied that it is safe to do so.

10.7.3. A rescue team and resuscitation equipment should be available for immediate action. The resuscitation equipment should be positioned ready for use at the entrance.

10.7.4. Only trained personnel should be assigned duties at entry, functioning as attendants or as members of rescue teams.

10.7.5. The number entering should be limited to those persons who actually need to work in the space and could be rescued in the event of an emergency.

10.7.6. At least one person, trained in entry procedures and the action to be taken in the event of an emergency, should be detailed to stay by the entrance whilst it is occupied.

10.7.7. A communication system should be agreed and tested by all involved, to ensure that persons entering the space can keep in touch with the person stationed at the entrance.

10.7.8. A communication system should be set up between the officer on watch and the person stationed at the entrance.

10.7.9. It should be checked that entry with breathing apparatus is possible before entry is allowed. The extent by which movement could be restricted, or the removal of a casualty could be hampered, by the use of breathing apparatus, lifelines or harnesses should be ascertained.

10.7.10. Rescue harness lifelines should be long enough for the purpose and easily detachable by the wearer, but should not otherwise come away from the harness.

10.8. Procedures and arrangements during entry

10.8.1. The space should be continuously ventilated whilst occupied and during temporary breaks. All persons in the space should leave it immediately should the ventilation system fail.

10.8.2. Whilst the space is occupied the atmosphere should be tested periodically. Should there be any deterioration in the conditions all persons should leave immediately.

10.8.3. Work should stop and all persons should leave the space if unforeseen difficulties or hazards occur. The situation should then be reassessed (see paragraph 10.6.1).

10.8.4. If any person working in a space feels in any way adversely affected he should give a pre-arranged signal to the person standing by the entrance and immediately leave the space.

10.8.5. A rescue harness should be worn to facilitate recovery in the event of an accident.

10.8.6. The general (or crew) alarm should be sounded in the event of an emergency, so that immediate back-up can be given to the rescue team.

10.9. Additional requirements for entry into a space where the atmosphere is suspect or known to be unsafe

10.9.1. Where the atmosphere is considered suspect or unsafe to enter without breathing apparatus and provided all reasonable attempts at gas-freeing have been carried out, entry may be made if this is essential for testing purposes, the working of the ship, the safety of life or the safety of the ship. The number of persons entering should be the minimum necessary to undertake the work.

10.9.2. Breathing apparatus should always be worn. Respirators must not be used because they do not provide a supply of clean air from a source independent of the atmosphere in the space.

10.9.3. Two air supplies, as described in section 10.10, should be available to the wearer of breathing apparatus, except in the case of emergency, or where this is impractical because movement in the space would be seriously impeded. A continuous supply provided from outside the space should normally be used. Should it prove necessary to change over to the self-contained supply, the person should immediately vacate the space.

10.9.4. Precautions should be taken to safeguard the continuity of the outside source of air during occupation of the space by the wearer of breathing apparatus. Special attention should be given to supplies originating from the engine-room.

10.9.5. A single air supply may be acceptable, where remote testing of the space is not reasonably practicable provided prolonged presence in the space is not required and the person is situated so that he can be hauled out immediately in case of emergency.

10.9.6. A rescue harness should be worn. Lifelines should be used where practicable, and should be attended by a person stationed at the entrance who has received training in how to pull an unconscious person from a dangerous space. If hoisting equipment would be needed to effect a rescue, the availability of persons to operate the equipment in the event of an emergency should be ensured.

10.9.7. Portable lights and other electrical equipment should be of a type approved for use in a flammable atmosphere.

10.9.8. Personal protective equipment should be worn where there is a hazard due to chemicals, in liquid, gaseous or vapour form.

10.9.9. A pre-arranged plan should be drawn up to deal with the rescue of collapsed persons within a dangerous space, which should take into account the design of the individual ship and of the equipment and manpower on board. The need to allocate personnel to relieve or back-up those first into the space should be considered.

10.9.10. If a person working in the space indicates that he is being affected by the atmosphere, using the agreed communication system, the person stationed by the entrance should immediately raise the alarm. On no account should the person stationed at the entrance to the space attempt to enter it before additional help has arrived. No one should attempt a rescue without wearing breathing apparatus and a rescue harness and, whenever possible, the use of a lifeline.

10.9.11. If air is being supplied through an air line to the person who has become unwell, an immediate check should be made that his air supply is being maintained at the correct pressure.

10.9.12. An incapacitated person should be removed from the space as quickly as possible, unless he is gravely injured, e.g. a broken back, when essential first-aid treatment should be administered first. The restoration of the casualty's air supply at the earliest possible moment must be the first priority.

10.10. Breathing apparatus and resuscitation equipment

10.10.1. Every seafarer likely to use breathing apparatus should be instructed in its use by a competent person.

10.10.2. The full, pre-wearing check and donning procedures recommended by the manufacturer should be undertaken by the master, or the responsible officer, and the person about to enter the space. In particular the following should be checked:

(a) that there will be sufficient clean air at the correct pressure;

(b) that low pressure alarms are working properly;

(c) that the face mask fits correctly against the user's face, so that, combined with pressure of the air coming into the mask, there will not be an ingress of oxygen-deficient air or toxic vapours when the user inhales. It should be noted that facial hair or spectacles may prevent the formation of an airtight seal between a person's face and the face mask;

(d) that the wearer of the breathing apparatus understands whether or not his air supply may be shared with another person and if so is also aware that such procedures should only be used in an extreme emergency;

(e) that when work is being undertaken in the space the wearer should keep the self-contained supply for use when there is a failure of the continuous supply from outside the space.

10.10.3. When in a dangerous space:

(a) no one should remove his own breathing apparatus;

(b) breathing apparatus should not be removed from a person unless it is necessary to do so to save his life.

10.10.4. Where any person may be required to enter a dangerous space appropriate resuscitators should be provided, and if entry is expected to occur at sea the ship should be provided with the appropriate equipment. If the appropriate equipment has not been provided entry should not take place.

10.11. Maintenance of equipment and training

10.11.1. A competent person should maintain and periodically inspect and check for correct operation all breathing apparatus, rescue harnesses, lifelines, resuscitation equipment and any other equipment provided for use in, or in connection with, entry into dangerous spaces or during emergencies. A record should be kept of the inspections and checks. All items of breathing apparatus should be inspected and checked for correct operation before and after use.

10.11.2. Equipment for testing the atmosphere of dangerous spaces should be kept in good working order and, where applicable, regularly serviced and calibrated. The manufacturer's recommendations should be kept with the equipment and should be followed.

10.11.3. Shipowners should provide seafarers with the necessary training, instructions and information on entry into dangerous spaces, which should include:

(a) recognition of the circumstances and activities likely to lead to the presence of a dangerous atmosphere;

(b) recognition of the hazards associated with entry into dangerous spaces, and the precautions to be taken;

(c) the use and proper care of equipment and clothing required for entry into dangerous spaces;

(d) instruction and drill in rescue from dangerous spaces.

11. Manual lifting and carrying

11.1. General provisions

11.1.1. Lifting and carrying objects may seem to be simple operations but many persons on board ship have sustained serious back and other injuries by lifting in an incorrect manner.

11.1.2. Every person who is required to handle loads manually should be properly trained.

11.1.3. Before lifting and carrying weights, seafarers should first inspect the load as regards its weight, size and shape. Attention should be given to sharp edges, protruding nails or splinters, greasy surfaces or any other features which might lead to an accident.

11.1.4. The size and shape of the load are not a reliable indication of its actual weight.

11.1.5. The area over which the load is to be moved should not be slippery and should be free from obstructions.

11.1.6. To ensure that the lift will be as straight as possible, a firm and balanced stance should be taken close to the load, with the feet being kept slightly apart.

11.1.7. Seafarers lifting a load from below knee level should adopt a crouching position with the knees bent but the back should be kept straight to ensure that the legs take the strain.

11.1.8. The load should be gripped with the whole of the hand.

11.1.9. The load should be kept close to the body and lifted by straightening the legs.

11.1.10. Where possible or when lifting to a high level, the seafarer should:

(a) use a bench or support to make the lift in two stages;

(b) adjust the grip as necessary for carrying or lifting to a second level.

11.1.11. The load should be carried in such a manner as to ensure that vision is not obscured.

11.1.12. To put the load down, the lifting procedure should be reversed, with the legs doing the work of lowering, with the knees bent, back straight and the load kept close to the body.

11.1.13. Safety shoes or boots should be worn.

11.1.14. Personal protective equipment such as back supports should be worn as much as possible.

11.1.15. Mechanical aids or devices, such as a block and tackle, should be used as much as possible.

11.1.16. Seafarers should take note of the working environment when loads are being carried on board ship, particularly if the ship is at sea.

11.1.17. Particular care should be taken to coordinate action when two or more people are carrying a load.

12. Tools and materials

12.1. General provisions[1]

12.1.1. Shipowners should ensure that all machines, tools and other equipment are suitable for the work in hand and the conditions in which they are to be used.

12.1.2. Personal protective equipment, e.g. eye, face, hearing protectors and hair nets for long hair, should be worn when appropriate.

12.2. Hand tools

12.2.1. Tools should be treated with due care and should be used only for the purpose for which each tool is designed.

12.2.2. Damaged or unsafe tools should not be used.

12.2.3. Tools that are not being used should be placed in a carrier, box or tool rack.

12.2.4. All tools should be stowed in lockers or other appropriate places at the end of a work period or operation.

12.3. Portable electric, pneumatic and hydraulic tools

12.3.1. Power-operated tools are dangerous if they are not maintained and operated correctly.

---

[1] Guidance on the training of engine-room officers and ratings in the use of tools may be found in section 25 of the *IMO/ILO Document for guidance: An international maritime training guide* (1985 or later edition).

12.3.2. Special care should be taken when seafarers work in damp conditions since the risk of electric shock is greatly increased in the presence of moisture or high humidity.

12.3.3. Since ships are largely made of metal, which conducts electricity, great care should be taken in the use of electrical tools.

12.3.4. Electrical tools designed to be earthed should be properly connected.

12.3.5. Electrical tools should be inspected before use and particular attention should be paid to power supply leads.

12.3.6. Electrical leads and hydraulic/pneumatic tool hoses should be kept clear of anything that might damage them.

12.3.7. Tool pieces, such as drills or bits, must be secure in the tool and must not be fixed or replaced while the tool is connected to a power source.

12.3.8. Power tools should be switched off and disconnected from the power source when not in use.

12.4. Workshop and bench machines (fixed installations)

12.4.1. No person should operate a machine unless authorized and trained to do so.

12.4.2. Machine operators should be competent in the use of the machine and familiar with its controls.

12.4.3. All dangerous parts of machines must be securely guarded.[1] Examples of "dangerous parts" are reciprocating components, revolving shafts, gearing, belt drives, etc.

---

[1] The Guarding of Machinery Recommendation, 1963 (No. 118), provides that no worker should use any machinery without the guards provided being in position nor make the guards inoperative for another worker.

12.4.4. A machine should be checked each time before use and the guards and safety devices should be inspected before the machine is started.

12.4.5. No control or light switch should be in such a position that an operator is required to lean over a machine to reach it.

12.4.6. Loose fitting and unsuitable clothing should not be worn when operating machines.

12.4.7. If a machine is found to be defective it should be isolated from its source until repaired by a competent person.

12.4.8. Working areas should be kept clean and uncluttered and debris such as metal turnings and swarf should not be allowed to build up around a machine.

12.4.9. A machine in use should never be left unattended, even for a few minutes, and should always be stopped when it is not being used.

12.4.10. Before a drill or lathe is started, the chuck key should be removed and the operator should ensure that other people are clear of the machine.

12.4.11. Workpieces for drilling and milling should be securely held at all times by a machine vice or clamp.

12.5. Abrasive wheels

12.5.1. Abrasive wheels should be selected, mounted and used only by competent persons and in accordance with the manufacturer's instructions.

12.5.2. A wheel should be closely inspected for damage and brushed clean before it is mounted.

12.5.3. The clamping nut should be tightened only enough to hold the wheel firmly.

12.5.4. A strong guard should be provided and kept in position at every abrasive wheel (unless the nature of the work absolutely precludes its use) both to contain the wheel parts in the event of a burst and to prevent an operator from coming into contact with the wheel.

12.5.5. The speed of the spindle should not exceed the stated maximum speed of the wheel and should be periodically checked.

12.5.6. When dry grind operations are being carried out or an abrasive wheel is being trued or dressed, suitable transparent screens should be fitted in front of the exposed part of the wheel or operators should wear properly fitting eye protectors.

12.6. Spirit lamps

12.6.1. Care should be taken in filling lamps. If a lamp has been in use it should be completely cool before it is refilled.

12.7. Compressed air

12.7.1. Compressed air should never be directed at any part of a person's body as air puncturing a person's skin could have serious consequences.

12.7.2. Compressed air should not be used to clean a working area.

12.7.3. Seafarers should be particularly aware of the dangers of using high pressure pneumatic equipment, such as cleaning and scaling devices, as their misuse can lead to fatal consequences.

12.8. Compressed gas cylinders

12.8.1. The stowage and carriage of compressed gas cylinders are governed by the IMDG code (see Chapter 7) to which reference should be made.

12.8.2. Cylinders should always be handled with care, whether full or empty.

12.8.3. Cylinders should be properly secured and kept upright but must be capable of quick release. Oxygen and fuel gas cylinders (such as acetylene) should be kept in suitable, separate, well-ventilated compartments that are not subject to extremes of temperature. The space should have no electrical fittings or other sources of ignition. "No smoking" signs should be displayed at the entrance and within the space.

12.8.4. Protective caps over the valve should be screwed in place when cylinders are not in use or are being moved. Valves should be closed when the cylinder is empty.

12.8.5. Cylinder valves, controls and associated fittings should be kept free from oil, grease and paint. Controls should not be operated with oily hands.

13. Welding, flame-cutting and other hot work

13.1. General provisions

13.1.1. Welding, flame-cutting and other hot work operations should be conducted within the "permit-to-work" system (see Chapter 4), whenever carried out in a non-workshop location.

13.1.2. Operators should be competent and familiar with the equipment to be used, which should be inspected by a competent person before use.

13.1.3. Seafarers should be given careful instructions if special precautions need to be taken.

13.1.4. Harmful fumes may be produced and oxygen depleted during operations. Special care should be taken during operations in enclosed places and enclosed space procedures (see Chapter 10) should be used where necessary to ensure safe operations.

13.1.5. An assistant should be in continuous attendance and be instructed in emergency procedures.

13.1.6. The precautions provided in Chapter 24 should be followed for hot work aboard tankers.

13.2. Personal protective equipment

13.2.1. Clean and approved personal protective equipment should be worn by the operator and other persons involved in the work process.

13.2.2. The operator should normally wear:

(a) a welding helmet and suitable eye shield;

(b) leather working gloves;

(c) a leather apron when appropriate; and

(d) other appropriate personal protective equipment.

13.3. Precautions against fire, explosions and non-life-supporting environments

13.3.1. Before any operation begins, inspections and tests should be carried out to ensure that there are no combustible solids, liquids or gases at or in any compartments adjacent to the work area which might be ignited by heat or sparks from the work.

13.3.2. All surfaces to be welded, or upon which hot work is to be conducted, should be free of oil, grease or any flammable or combustible material.

13.3.3. All openings through which sparks might fall should be closed where practical.

13.3.4. Cargo tanks, fuel tanks, cargo holds or other tanks or spaces (including cargo pumps and pipelines) that have contained flammable substances should be certified by a competent person as being free of flammable gases before any work commences (see Chapter 4).

13.3.5. All operations should be properly supervised and a fire watch maintained, both in the operational area and all adjacent areas, including spaces on the other side of affected bulkheads. Because of the possibility of delayed fires the fire watch should be maintained for a suitable period of time after the work has been completed.

13.3.6. Suitable fire extinguishers should be kept at hand.

13.4. Electric welding equipment

13.4.1. Power sources should have a direct current (DC) which minimizes the risk from electric shock.

13.4.2. The "go and return" system in which the welding set has two cables should be used, with the "return" cable being separately earthed to the ship's structure. The lead and return cables should be of the shortest length possible (and of an appropriate cross-section) to avoid voltage drop.

13.4.3. Cables should be inspected before use and connectors should be fully insulated.

13.4.4. Suitable means should be provided for rapidly cutting off current from the electrode should the operator encounter difficulties.

13.5. Precautions to be taken during electric-arc welding

13.5.1. Non-conducting safety footwear should be worn in addition to the personal protective equipment specified in section 13.2. Clothing should be kept as dry as possible.

13.5.2. If the operator is in close contact with the ship's structure, protection should be provided by dry insulating mats or boards.

13.5.3. Welding should not be carried out in hot/humid conditions which might cause sweat or damp clothing.

13.5.4. Under no circumstances whatsoever should a welder work in wet conditions.

13.5.5. The electrode holder should be isolated from the current supply before a used electrode is removed and before a new electrode is inserted. This precaution is necessary because some electrode coatings have extremely low resistance.

13.6. Flame-cutting and brazing

13.6.1. Equipment should have back pressure valves fitted adjacent to the torch in the oxygen and acetylene lines and flame arrestors fitted at the low pressure side of the regulators.

13.6.2. Oxygen pressure should always be sufficient to prevent acetylene from entering the oxygen line.

13.6.3. Acetylene may explode under excessive pressure. It should not be used at a pressure exceeding 1 atmosphere gauge.

13.6.4. If a backfire occurs, the valves on the oxygen and acetylene cylinders should be closed immediately. Personnel should be trained in the appropriate methods for cooling and/or jettisoning cylinders which become hot. An acetylene cylinder which becomes overheated is very dangerous as an impact could cause internal ignition and subsequent explosion.

13.6.5. Only hoses which have been specially designed for flame-cutting and brazing operations should be used; hoses in which a flashback has occurred should be discarded.

13.6.6. Blowpipes should be lit by safe means such as a stationary pilot flame or a special friction igniter.

13.6.7. Gases should be shut off at the pressure-reducing regulators before a blowpipe is changed.

14. Painting

14.1. General provisions

14.1.1. Paints may contain toxic or irritant substances and a paint for which no manufacturer's information is available should not be used.

14.1.2. Some paints dry by evaporation of the paint's solvent and the process may cause flammable or toxic vapours. All interior and enclosed spaces should be well ventilated while painting is in progress and until the paint has dried.

14.1.3. Smoking should not be permitted during painting. Naked lights, such as matches, should not be used in spaces until paint has fully dried.

14.1.4. Great care should be taken when mixing two-pack (two component) paint as a chemical reaction takes place during the mixing which might create heat and fumes.

14.1.5. Chemical rust removers are corrosive and precautions should be taken to protect eyes and skin.

14.1.6. Spaces where paint and painting equipment are stored should be well ventilated. (See section 10.9 for guidance concerning entry into such spaces when the ventilation system is inoperative.)

14.2. Spraying

14.2.1. Personnel should closely follow the manufacturer's instructions on the operation of spray equipment.

14.2.2. A "paint mist" may form during spraying operations and personnel should wear suitable personal protective equipment such as a combination suit, hood, gloves and eye protectors. A respirator may also be necessary.

14.2.3. Paints containing mercury, lead or any toxic compounds should not be sprayed in interior spaces.

14.2.4. Airless spray equipment ejects paint at a very high pressure. The operation is hazardous as the paint can penetrate the skin or cause eye injuries. Great care should be taken in the use of such equipment.

14.2.5. Seafarers should be trained in the correct methods of unblocking nozzles according to the manufacturer's instructions.

14.3. Painting aloft and working over the side

14.3.1. Chapter 15 should be read for the precautions to be taken when working aloft and over the side.

15. Working aloft and over the side

15.1. General provisions

15.1.1. Consideration should be given to a permit-to-work system for work aloft or over the side depending on the nature of the work (see Chapter 4). A form for working aloft should take account of the particular nature of the operation.

15.1.2. Particular attention should be paid to sea and weather conditions and the possibility of squalls before working aloft or over the side is commenced. In general, working aloft or over the side should not be permitted if the movement of a ship in a seaway makes such work hazardous.

15.1.3. In coastal waters strong tidal or current rips could cause sudden, unexpected ship movements which might be hazardous to seafarers working aloft.

15.1.4. Special consideration should be given to the problems of working near the ship's whistle, funnel, radio aerials and radar scanners. All relevant officers should be informed before work commences and all relevant equipment should be isolated, shut down or appropriate procedures adopted. Warning notices should be posted as appropriate. Officers should be informed when the work is completed.

15.1.5. Young or inexperienced persons should not be required to work aloft or over the side unless accompanied by an experienced seafarer or under adequate supervision.

15.1.6. All seafarers should wear safety harnesses and safety nets should be rigged where appropriate. Persons working over the side should wear life-jackets or other suitable flotation devices. Someone should be in attendance on deck and a lifebuoy with a line attached should be readily available.

15.1.7. Warning notices that seafarers are working aloft should be posted on deck and elsewhere as appropriate. Tools should not be carried in pockets but secured in belt tool carriers and they should be kept secured to the belt with a lanyard or string during the work. Tools and stores should be sent up and lowered by line in suitable containers.

15.1.8. All equipment, such as lizards, blocks and gantlines, should be carefully examined before use and if there is any doubt as to the standard, quality and condition of any item it should not be used.

15.1.9. Where possible, only permanent fixtures to the ship's structure, such as welded eye pads, should be used as securing points for lizards, blocks and gantlines.

15.1.10. Lizards and gantlines should be away from, or protected from, sharp edges.

15.1.11. Cargo handling operations should not take place in the vicinity where seafarers are working aloft.

15.1.12. Seafarers working aloft or over the side should be continuously supervised by a competent person.

15.2. Cradles and stages

15.2.1. Cradles should be at least 40 cm wide and fitted with guard-rails to a height of 1 m.

15.2.2. Plank stages should be made from sound wood and materials and should be free from defect.

15.2.3. As far as possible stages should be secured against movement.

15.2.4. Gantlines should be long enough to allow stages to be lowered to a level which enables seafarers to step off the stage easily.

15.2.5. When seafarers working on a stage are required to lower the stage themselves, all movements of the stage should be small and carefully controlled.

15.3. Bosun's chairs

15.3.1. A hook should not be used to secure a bosun's chair unless it is a type which cannot be accidentally dislodged.

15.3.2. A chair used with a gantline should be secured with a double sheet bend and the loose end should be tucked into the rope lay of the standing part.

15.3.3. A chair, and all associated equipment such as gantlines, should be carefully inspected before use and a load test applied before hoisting takes place. If it is necessary to hoist a person aloft, it should be done only by hand and never by mechanical means, such as a winch.

15.3.4. Seafarers should be reminded that when securing the hitch in a chair the practice of holding both parts of the gantline with one hand and making the lowering hitch with the other is dangerous.

15.4. Ropes

15.4.1. The safety of seafarers working aloft depends to a large extent on the condition of the ropes used in the operations. Such ropes must be given considerable care and attention (see also Chapter 18).

15.4.2. Ropes should be stowed in a special locker and used for no other purpose than for working aloft. Nothing else should be stowed in the locker; stores such as detergents and paints may damage ropes. The locker should be dry and not subject to excessive heat.

15.4.3. All ropes should be thoroughly inspected each time before use and daily when in use. It should be remembered that although the surface of a rope may indicate that it is in good condition, it may have deteriorated inside.

15.4.4. All ropes (e.g. gantlines, lifelines and lizards) should be load tested before use to four or five times the weight that they will be expected to carry.

15.5. Portable ladders

15.5.1. Working from ladders, where there is a risk of overstretching and falling, should be discouraged.

15.5.2. A safety harness secured above the person should be used when working aloft.

15.5.3. The ladder should extend to a height of at least 1 m above the top landing place.

15.5.4. (1) A ladder should be effectively secured so that it cannot move.

(2) Seafarers using a ladder should:

(a)   have both hands free for climbing up and down;

(b)   face a rigid ladder when climbing up and down;

(c)   not carry tools or equipment.

15.5.5. Rigid portable ladders should be placed at an angle between 65 and 70 degrees to the horizontal and there should be a clearance of at least 15 cm behind all the rungs.

15.6. Rope ladders

15.6.1. Rope ladders should be of good construction, adequate strength and properly maintained.

15.6.2. The rope ladder should be properly secured but never secured to railings, or to any other means of support, unless the railings or support will safely take the weight of a person and the ladder.

15.6.3. The rope ladder should either hang fully extended or be pulled up completely: it should never be left so that slack may suddenly pay out when the ladder is used.

15.6.4. The ladder should be rigged and used under the supervision of a responsible person.

15.7. Working over the side from punts

15.7.1. Punts should be stable and have suitable fencing.

15.7.2. The person in charge should consider the potential hazards of working at the stern and near side discharges and the hazards of strong tides and wash from passing vessels, etc. All relevant persons should be informed that the work is taking place.

15.7.3. A person painting over the side should wear a lifeline and a buoyancy garment. Someone should be in attendance on deck and a lifebuoy with a line attached should be readily available.

16. Working with electricity and electrical equipment

16.1. General provisions

16.1.1. All relevant national and international regulations governing the design and construction of electrical installations should be observed, with account being taken of unusual conditions which may be encountered in service.[1]

16.1.2. Seafarers should receive adequate training before being permitted to work on electrical installations.[2]

16.1.3. The installation should be maintained and protected to minimize the possibility of fire, external explosion, electrical shocks and danger to seafarers.

16.1.4. All live parts should be effectively insulated and enclosed in conduits or otherwise protected and should be maintained in that condition.

16.1.5. All electrical equipment should be regularly inspected to ensure that it is suitable for its intended use. Any electrical faults or other defects should be immediately reported to the appropriate person and repaired by a competent person.

---

[1] Examples of such conditions are exposure to:

(a) moisture, steam and oil vapour, salt-laden atmosphere, sea spray, high winds and ice formation;

(b) abnormal vibrations, deformation and mechanical shock;

(c) unusually high or low temperatures; and

(d) explosive mixtures when used in certain areas.

[2] Section 24 of the *IMO/ILO Document for guidance: An international maritime training guide* (1985 or later edition) provides information on training requirements.

16.1.6. Attention should be paid to the maintenance of the emergency source of electrical power.

16.1.7. All electrical appliances should be clearly marked to indicate their safe operating voltage.

16.1.8. Flickering lights should be investigated and repaired by a competent person.

16.1.9. Circuits and appliances carrying different voltages in the same installation should be clearly distinguishable by notices, markings on distribution boxes and other conspicuous means.

16.1.10. Seafarers should not interfere with a design and installation intended to prevent circuits and apparatus from being subjected to voltages which exceed those for which they were designed.

16.1.11. Repairs to electrical installations should be carried out only by a competent person or when a "permit-to-work" has been issued (see Chapter 4).

16.1.12. Effective means of ensuring safe isolation of every circuit, subcircuit and apparatus, such as facilities to lock off isolators, key control or signing, should be provided to minimize or eliminate danger to seafarers.

16.1.13. Every circuit should be protected against overload currents, so as to reduce damage to the system and keep the danger of fire to a minimum.

16.1.14. Redundant circuits or apparatus should be disconnected or dismantled.

16.1.15. Personal protective equipment, such as rubber gloves and rubber boots, should be used whenever there is a risk of electric shock, but should not be regarded as providing full protection against such a risk.

16.1.16. Protection against contact with live equipment should be afforded by:

(a) placing live parts out of reach;
(b) effective enclosure of live parts; and
(c) adequate insulation.

16.1.17. The enclosures of live circuits, such as terminal boxes, should be designed so that they can be removed only by authorized persons.

16.1.18. Suitable fuses or contact-breakers should be placed in each circuit to limit the current to the safe rating for the cable or equipment.

16.1.19. Where fuses are used, they should bear clear markings indicating their rated current and, as far as practicable, their rated capacity. Replacement fuses should be of the correct rating.

16.1.20. Fuses should be replaced only by authorized persons.

16.1.21. All fuses should be protected to prevent accidental contact.

16.1.22. Effective means should be employed to ensure that persons removing or inserting fuses will not be endangered, in particular, by any adjacent live parts.

16.1.23. In general it should not be possible to remove or insert fuses in a circuit unless it has been made dead by means of an isolating device on the incoming side.

16.1.24. The following notices should be exhibited at suitable places:

(a) a warning notice prohibiting unauthorized persons from entering electrical equipment rooms, interfering with switchboards, and handling or interfering with electrical apparatus;
(b) a warning notice specifying the person to be notified in the event of an electrical accident or some other dangerous occurrence, and indicating how to communicate with that person;

(c) a notice specifying the voltage present in equipment or conductors; and

(d) a notice prohibiting the use of naked flames in the vicinity of the battery room.

16.1.25. Only authorized persons should have access to and enter equipment rooms containing live electrical equipment or have access to the rear of live switchboards.

16.1.26. No work should be done in dangerous proximity to a conductor or installation until it has been made dead and signs have been suitably posted.

16.1.27. (1) If a conductor or an installation is in the immediate vicinity of a work location and cannot be made dead, special precautions should be taken.

(2) Any such operation should be supervised by a competent person.

16.1.28. All conductors and equipment should be considered to be live unless there is definite proof to the contrary.

16.1.29. Before the current is restored, a competent person should ensure that no seafarers remain in a dangerous position.

16.1.30. After work has been done on electrical equipment, the current should be switched on again only by, or on the orders of, a competent person.

16.1.31. Distribution apparatus and switch gear should be protected in all circumstances, particularly:

(a) against dripping or splashing of water; and

(b) in switchboard rooms and machinery spaces.

16.1.32. If temporary connections have to be made while repairs are being carried out, the connections should be made with cables having an adequate margin of current and voltage rating and by a competent person. They should be disconnected and removed as soon as they are no longer required.

16.1.33. Seafarers not authorized to carry out electrical work should never install new equipment or alter existing equipment.

16.2. Wandering leads, portable lights, electric tools and other movable equipment

16.2.1. All flexible cables should be:

(a) of sufficient size and current rating for the purposes for which they are to be used;

(b) so constructed, insulated, secured and protected as to ensure that danger to seafarers will be reduced to a minimum.

16.2.2. Every electrical connection should be of suitable construction with regard to conductivity, insulation, mechanical strength and protection, with account being taken of the need to use such equipment in exposed locations.

16.2.3. (1) Cables and conductors should be mechanically protected and properly and durably insulated at points where they are joined, branched or led into any apparatus.

(2) For these purposes junction boxes, sleeves, bushings, glands or equivalent connecting devices should be employed.

(3) Where practicable, flexible cables should be joined by junction boxes or plug and socket couplings, and the attachment should be made by screwing, clamping, soldering, rivetting, brazing and crimping or equivalent means.

(4) Where armoured cables are joined, care should be taken to continue the conductive bond between the armouring of the cables by the bridging and the junction boxes.

16.2.4. All conductors and apparatus liable to be exposed to a flammable or explosive atmosphere should be so constructed as to negate the possibility of ignition of the vapour.

16.2.5. The supply voltage to portable tools and appliances should generally not exceed 240 volts.

16.2.6. Hand-held electrical tools should be provided with a spring-loaded switch that will break the circuit automatically when the tool is released from the hand.

16.2.7. Portable electrical tools and appliances should not be used in a potentially flammable or explosive atmosphere, unless they are of a type certificated for use in such an atmosphere and the action is authorized by a responsible officer.

16.2.8. A hand lamp or other portable lamp should be of an approved type with effective protection for the bulb and with a suitable cover of glass or other transparent material. Such equipment should be dust and water proof and, where necessary, gas proof.

16.2.9. Flexible cables should:

(a) not be laid on surfaces that are oily or wet with corrosive liquids;

(b) be kept clear of moving loads, running gear and moving equipment;

(c) not be used to lift the portable lamp or portable tools to which they are connected;

(d) have additional protection where they are likely to be subjected to rough usage or moisture.

16.2.10. When seafarers use portable equipment or portable lamps they should ensure that any flexible cables passing through doors, hatches, manholes, etc., are protected and that their insulation is not damaged by the closing of doors, covers or lids.

16.3. High-voltage systems

16.3.1. As high-voltage systems present considerable danger they should be worked upon only by specially trained and certified seafarers.

16.3.2. Manufacturer's instruction manuals should be provided for all high-voltage equipment and be closely followed.

16.3.3. Care should be taken to observe the requirement that all high-voltage equipment should be enclosed or protected so that access can be obtained only by authorized persons using a special tool or key that is retained by a competent person, unless the equipment is designed in a way to ensure that any attempt at access will automatically isolate and render it safe.

16.4. Rectifiers and electronic equipment

16.4.1. No maintenance or repair work should be attempted until the equipment has been effectively isolated and any stored energy dissipated.

16.4.2. Special attention should be paid to the hazard of working near charged capacitors associated with rectification circuits.

16.4.3. Only competent persons should be authorized to repair electronic equipment.

16.5. Radio communication equipment

16.5.1. Aerials and open wire feeders should be placed and guarded in a way to make them inaccessible to unauthorized persons.

16.5.2. Conductors that pass through areas of high electromagnetic flux should be insulated or otherwise protected in areas to which seafarers have access.

16.5.3. Any work in the vicinity of transmitting aerials should be carried out only within the "permit-to-work" system (see Chapter 4). Warning notices should be posted at appropriate places until the work has been completed.

16.5.4. No seafarers should be allowed to work in the vicinity of transmitting aerials whilst there is a possibility that such aerials may be energized.

16.5.5. Suitable means should be provided and maintained to exclude any persons from the vicinity of equipment where there is a danger from shock, radio frequency burns and injury from X-rays or other radiation.

16.6. Batteries and battery rooms

16.6.1. Battery rooms should be adequately ventilated to avoid accumulation of explosive gases.

16.6.2. Light fittings and any electrical equipment in the battery room should be of a type certified as being suitable for a hydrogen atmosphere.

16.6.3. Particular hazards when charging batteries are hydrogen explosion and short circuits. During charging, a battery gives off hydrogen and oxygen and the subsequent mixture can be easily ignited. Short circuits may cause arcing which could lead to an explosion or burn seafarers.

16.6.4. Only authorized persons should enter battery rooms and, when doing so, they should ensure that they do not introduce any source of ignition. Smoking is prohibited in battery rooms.

16.6.5. Care should be taken when using metal tools or implements to avoid making contact with the metal battery case or terminals.

16.6.6. Battery rooms should be kept clear of any equipment, including any other electrical equipment, likely to act as a source of ignition, and should not be used as storerooms.

16.6.7. Lead-acid batteries and alkaline batteries should not be stored in the same room because of the possible interaction of the electrolytes.

16.6.8. Safe and effective means of inspecting and servicing the batteries should be provided by adequate lighting and access to each cell, and personal protective clothing, gloves and goggles should be supplied and worn by seafarers engaged in topping up the batteries. Warning: Open flames and naked lights should not be used to inspect battery cells.

16.7. Work with visual display units (VDUs),[1] including microcomputers

16.7.1. Seafarers should be given adequate individual training in the use and capabilities of VDUs and microcomputers.

16.7.2. Work with VDUs can be mentally tiring and measures should be taken to minimize the risk of eyestrain. Lighting should be adequate for the task, with glare and reflection cut to a minimum, and the display screen should be clear and easy to read. Rest periods should be provided.

16.7.3. Symptoms such as neck and arm pains may arise as the result of bad posture. VDU operators should avoid sitting in a slumped or cramped position and should be provided with an adjustable chair. Screens and keyboards should be adjustable to the correct height and the correct distance from the operator.

---

[1] Further information on this subject may be found in the ILO publication *Working with visual display units,* Occupational Safety and Health Series No. 61 (Geneva, 1990).

17. Working with dangerous and irritating substances and radiations[1]

17.1. General provisions

17.1.1. This chapter should be read in conjunction with Chapter 7 which refers to publications and codes containing essential information on the handling of dangerous goods.

17.1.2. Dangerous and irritating substances should be handled only under the supervision of a responsible officer.

17.1.3. Seafarers should wear appropriate personal protective equipment (see Chapter 5).

17.1.4. Seafarers should be aware that materials such as residual fuel oil and used or spent engine oil contain substances known to be carcinogenic. In addition to any carcinogenic effects, contact between oil and human skin may lead to a range of skin complaints ranging from mild irritation to severe oil acne. Contact must be avoided by taking suitable precautions, e.g. the owner should provide barrier creams and personal protective equipment.

17.1.5. Masters should ensure that the data sheet information provided by the manufacturers with their products is made available to all seafarers who may come into contact with these products.

---

[1] Detailed guidance on protecting workers from these and other substances may be obtained from the following ILO publications: *Occupational exposure limits for airborne toxic substances,* Occupational Safety and Health Series No. 37, third edition (Geneva, 1991), and *The provision of the basic safety standards for radiation protection relevant to the protection of workers against ionizing radiation*, Occupational Safety and Health Series No. 55 (Geneva, 1985).

17.2. Work with unsaturated polyesters

17.2.1. Composite bonding material can contain unsaturated polyesters which may cause skin irritation which can be difficult to control. Appropriate personal protective clothing should be worn when using substances which contain unsaturated polyesters.

17.3. Work with adhesives

17.3.1. Many adhesives emit fumes which are detrimental to health. Appropriate respiratory equipment should be worn and work spaces should be well ventilated.

17.3.2. Fire precautions should be observed when working with adhesives.

17.3.3. Some adhesives, such as "super-glues", can bond skin upon contact. Such adhesives should be used with great caution and the manufacturer's instructions should be closely followed if skin becomes bonded to objects or to other parts of the body. Force should never be used to separate skin or to detach skin from objects.

17.3.4. Under no circumstances should "super-glues" be used for the purposes of practical jokes.

17.4. Removing insulation, paint and other coatings

17.4.1. When possible, information on the nature of the material should be obtained and any particular hazards identified and suitable precautions taken.

17.4.2. Even seemingly innocuous material may contain harmful substances of which seafarers are unaware. Appropriate personal protective equipment should always be worn when insulation, paint and other coating are removed.

17.5. Work with asbestos[1]

17.5.1. All types of asbestos have a fibrous structure which can produce dust harmful to health if the surface integrity is damaged or disturbed. The danger is from minute fibres which can become lodged in the lungs and may cause cancer at a later period. (See also paragraph 5.1.5.)

17.5.2. Seafarers should be supplied with information if asbestos is on board ship. Such information should indicate the specific location.

17.5.3. Asbestos which is sealed is unlikely to release dust; old asbestos may be in poor condition and consideration should be given to its removal.

17.5.4. In general, asbestos should be removed only by a specialist removal contractor.

17.5.5. If it is necessary to carry out emergency repairs involving the removal of asbestos, full personal protective equipment, including respirators, should be worn and asbestos-handling safety procedures should be followed. If necessary expert advice should be sought.

17.6. Work with man-made mineral fibres

17.6.1. Man-made mineral fibres, such as those found within insulation material, can cause skin, nose and eye irritation. Appropriate personal protective equipment, such as goggles, masks and coveralls should be worn when handling such material.

---

[1] See also the Asbestos Convention, 1986 (No. 162). Further guidance may be obtained from the ILO *Code of Practice on Safety in the Use of Asbestos* (Geneva, 1984).

17.7. Radio and radar installations

17.7.1. Warning notices of the danger of high voltages should be located near radio transmitter aerials and lead-through insulators.

17.7.2. When seafarers are working near aerials and scanners, equipment should be isolated from the mains supply and radio transmitters earthed. Warning notices should be displayed on the relevant equipment.

17.7.3. Fuses should be removed from any equipment upon which work is to be carried out before that work commences.

17.8. Ionizing radiations[1]

17.8.1. Seafarers should not be exposed to dangerous levels of microwave radiation. Instructions contained in manufacturers' manuals should be strictly followed.

17.8.2. Eyes are particularly sensitive to microwave and ultrawave radiation. Care should be taken not to look into a radar scanner or waveguide when a radar is operating.

17.8.3. No work should be carried out within the marked safety radius of a satellite terminal antenna unless its transmitter has been switched off.

---

[1] See also Radiation Protection Convention, 1960 (No. 115). Further information on this subject may be obtained from the ILO publication *Protection of workers against radio frequency and microwave radiation: A technical review*, Occupational Safety and Health Series No. 57 (Geneva, 1986).

18. Upkeep of wire and fibre ropes[1]

18.1. General provisions

18.1.1. All ropes should be of sound material, good construction and adequate strength for the service required.

18.1.2. Before use, all ropes should be inspected and confirmed adequate for the intended working load.

18.1.3. All ropes used for load-bearing purposes should be periodically inspected by a competent person.

18.1.4. When any rope has been lengthened, altered or repaired, it should be examined and tested as necessary before it is used again.

18.1.5. (1) All ropes should be maintained in good order.

(2) When not in use they should be stowed under cover in clean, dry and well-ventilated places.

(3) Ropes should not be exposed to excessive heat or harmful chemicals.

18.1.6. (1) Care should be taken to avoid damaging or weakening a rope through:

(a) excessive stress and strain;

(b) rubbing or chafing against sharp objects; or

(c) passing it through too small a sheave or block.

---

[1] The ILO *Code of Practice on Safety and Health in Dock Work* contains further guidance on the upkeep of wire and fibre ropes, particularly ropes used with lifting and other cargo-handling equipment.

(2) Care should be taken to avoid the formation of a kink in any rope under strain.

18.1.7. (1) Care should be taken in withdrawing rope from a new coil.

(2) For stranded rope this should be done from the inside of a coil, taking it counter-clockwise for a rope for right-hand lay in order to retain the twist.

(3) Kinks should always be taken out by correct coiling (a right-hand coiling for a right-hand rope).

18.1.8. Any rope, whether natural, synthetic or wire, and of any construction, should not be put under a load suddenly or taken up with a jerk, since such action may overload it.

18.1.9. Where thimbles are required for eye splices on ropes, they should be of suitable size.

18.1.10. Rope ends and splices should be properly seized with yarn or other suitable means.

18.2. Wire ropes

18.2.1. No wire rope should be accepted on board unless it is accompanied by a certificate stating that it has been made to a recognized national or international standard and which gives details of its construction, safe working load and minimum breaking strain.

18.2.2. (1) Wire rope should always be handled with great care.

(2) Gloves should be used to protect hands against injury from wire ropes. However, when the rope is under stress or is being paid out, there is a danger that gloves may catch and cause severance of the hand or fingers. If gloves are not worn because of this concern, care should be taken to avoid hand injuries from broken or frayed strands.

18.2.3. (1) All wire ropes should be treated at regular intervals with suitable lubricants free from acid or alkali and, if possible, of a type recommended by the manufacturer.

(2) They should be regularly inspected for loose or broken strands or internal damage. Special attention should be paid to the condition of eye splices.

(3) Wire ropes should be stored on reels of suitable diameter.

(4) When a wire rope normally stored on reels is required for use it should be taken from the reel and flaked on the deck in a safe manner and inspected thoroughly for corrosion, damage, etc., and for the expiry of shelf-life which may have been recommended by the manufacturer.

18.2.4. A wire rope should not be used if:

(a) it shows signs of corrosion;

(b) there is a tendency towards separation of the strands or wires;

(c) excessive wear is indicated by flats appearing on the individual wires;

(d) there is excessive reduction in the measured diameter;

(e) the number of broken wires in any length of 10 diameters exceeds 5 per cent of the total number of wires in the rope;

(f) its statutory life or service life as recommended by the manufacturer has expired, although the wire may outwardly look good; or

(g) after failing any tests.

18.3. Fibre ropes

18.3.1. (1) At regular intervals and always after any cutting or splicing, fibre ropes used for hoisting purposes should be examined for abrasions, broken fibres, cuts, fraying, displacement of the yarns, discolouration and other defects.

(2) Contact with grit or sand or dragging over rough surfaces may damage rope and should be avoided.

18.3.2. (1) An eye or rope splice in a rope of natural fibre should have not less than three tucks.

(2) The tail of each tuck should be whipped in a suitable manner.

18.3.3. Ropes used in connection with safety equipment should preferably be of natural fibre.

18.3.4. If ropes of man-made fibre are used for life-saving purposes, they should:

(a) be approved for the purpose; and

(b) carry a means of identification that they are of the approved quality.

18.3.5. In using ropes of man-made fibres, seafarers should:

(a) avoid practices under which the special characteristics of such ropes could pose a hazard;

(b) be aware of the whiplash effects of a breakage in ropes of man-made fibre resulting from their added elasticity and lack of warning signs prior to breakage;

(c) avoid operations by which friction can heat the strands of the rope and produce a partial melting or stickiness in operation, as for example during surging or slacking away on a drum end or winch barrel, excessive angle around or movement over bollards or fairleads, or rubbing against or across a wire rope or hatch coaming;

(d) ensure that the manufacturer's recommendations concerning man-made fibre ropes are used when surging operations are carried out using winch drums to avoid excessive slippage;

(e) ensure that when taking in or paying out rope, slippage between the rope and the drum or barrel is reduced to a minimum;

(f) avoid gripping any rope that has become heated by friction;

(g) not allow ropes to run freely through their hands; and

(h) ensure that such ropes are not unduly exposed to injurious sunlight or harmful chemicals.

18.3.6. Man-made fibre ropes should be replaced when worn or damaged and in any case as required by the competent authority.

18.3.7. The method of making eye or loop splices in ropes of man-made fibre should accord strictly with the manufacturer's instructions for the particular material of which the rope is made.

18.3.8. Any part of a rope composed of man-made fibres, which has come into contact with such organic solvents as paint stripper or paint, should be discarded.

18.3.9. If a man-made rope has been subjected to a severe shock, it should be carefully examined.

18.3.10. A natural fibre rope that has become wet should be allowed to dry naturally.

18.3.11. A natural fibre rope that has been, or is suspected of having been, in contact with any acid, alkali or any other substance known to be detrimental to rope fibre should be taken out of service and destroyed.

19. Anchoring, docking and mooring[1]

19.1. General provisions

19.1.1. All anchoring, docking and mooring work should be supervised by a competent person, who must be in constant communication with the bridge.

19.1.2. (1) The windlass, anchors, chains, mooring lines and wires should be carefully maintained and regularly inspected for damage and defects.

(2) They should be periodically tested in accordance with the requirements of the competent authority.

19.1.3. Appropriate personal protective equipment should be provided to all seafarers involved in these operations.

19.1.4. Seafarers should be aware that it is usual for capstans, winches, or windlasses to be designed so as to stall or pay out before exceeding the safe working load of the weakest part of the system. Seafarers should not tamper with such arrangements.

19.2. Anchoring

19.2.1. Any anchor or chain showing defects should be withdrawn from service and repaired only by properly qualified persons.

19.2.2. In general, the anchor should not be dropped from the hawsepipe but should be walked back to a suitable position and let go from that position.

---

[1] The publication *Effective mooring* (London, 1989) of the International Chamber of Shipping provides further guidance on this topic.

19.2.3. Anchors may be let go at inappropriate moments due to the wrong message being received on a portable transceiver. All instructions should be "identified" by some means, e.g. by including the name of the vessel in the instruction.

19.2.4. Seafarers engaged in operating the brake, and others in the vicinity should wear goggles and safety helmets for protection from dust and debris thrown from the chain.

19.2.5. Seafarers engaged in stowing an anchor chain into the locker should stand in a protected position and should keep in constant communication with the windlass operator.

19.2.6. Anchors housed and not required should be properly secured to guard against accidents or damage should the windlass brake be released inadvertently.

19.3. Characteristics of man-made fibre ropes used for mooring or towing

19.3.1. Man-made fibre ropes have advantages over natural fibre ropes in terms of strength, durability and resistance to rot, etc. However, wear, damage and excessive exposure to sunlight can greatly diminish the strength of man-made ropes which should therefore be handled with care.

19.3.2. The following features should be taken into account when man-made ropes are used in port operations:

(a) owing to the ability of the ropes to stretch there may be considerable whiplash effect if the rope breaks;

(b) there is generally no audible warning prior to a rope breaking;

(c) some ropes have a low melting point and have a tendency to melt or fuse on a drum end.

19.4. Mooring and unmooring

19.4.1. All seafarers involved in mooring and unmooring operations of any kind should be informed of the hazards of engaging in such operations.

19.4.2. A competent person should be in charge of mooring operations and ascertain that there are no persons in a dangerous position before any heaving or letting go operation is commenced.

19.4.3. On each occasion that a vessel berths, all relevant circumstances such as weather, tides, passing vessels, etc., should be considered in determining a safe securing pattern of ropes and wires.

19.4.4. Mixed moorings of wires and ropes in the same direction should not be used because wires and ropes stretch differently.

19.4.5. There should be sufficient seafarers available to ensure the safe conduct of operations.

19.4.6. Only competent persons should operate windlasses and winches.

19.4.7. Under no circumstances whatsoever should seafarers stand in a bight of a rope or wire which is lying on deck. Seafarers should never stand or move across a rope or wire that is under strain.

19.4.8. Ropes and wires are frequently under strain during mooring operations and seafarers should, as much as possible, always stand in a place of safety from whiplash should ropes or wires break.

19.4.9. Due to the types of man-made ropes that may be on board ship, seafarers should be trained in the techniques of "stopping off" wires and ropes. Chain-securing devices should be used for stopping off wire mooring ropes but never for fibre ropes.

19.4.10. A watchman should regularly inspect the moorings when a vessel is alongside and the moorings should be kept tight at all times to prevent the ship's movement.

19.5. Mooring to buoys

19.5.1. Where mooring to buoys by the ship's crew is permitted by the local authority, the following additional precautions should be followed:

(a) lifebuoys, with and without attached lines, should be readily available;

(b) seafarers engaged in mooring to buoys from a ship's boat should wear personal protective equipment and a life-jacket;

(c) equipment should be provided to enable anyone who falls into the water to climb on board the boat;

(d) the eye of a slip wire used for mooring to buoys should never be put over the bitts;

(e) mooring strong points, such as chain-securing devices and quick-release mechanisms, should be maintained in a serviceable condition.

20. Working on deck or in cargo spaces

20.1. General provisions

20.1.1. All national and international requirements relating to the equipment used should be observed. However, when the ship is not subject to such requirements, they may nevertheless serve as useful guidance.

20.1.2. Reference should also be made to the chapters concerning special types of ships, where relevant.

20.1.3. All operations should be under the control of a responsible officer or experienced seafarer who should provide instruction and draw attention to any possible hazards associated with the operation.

20.1.4. No work should be started in adverse weather conditions.

20.1.5. If any operation is likely to involve a degree of risk to the safety and health of seafarers, it should be conducted only under the "permit-to-work" system (see Chapter 4).

20.1.6. When seafarers are to work on deck while a ship is at sea, a responsible person should authorize such work.

20.2. Cargo operations[1]

20.2.1. The following section applies to seafarers only to the extent that they are permitted to perform such cargo operations under applicable local regulations and/or practice.

---

[1] The ILO *Code of Practice on Safety and Health in Dock Work*, which goes into much greater detail on safety requirements and equipment specifications for cargo handling equipment, especially equipment used on general cargo ships, should be used in conjunction with this code.

20.2.2. This section outlines general considerations for cargo operations. For additional information on cargo operations on specific types of ships, reference should be made to Chapter 24. The guidance provided in Chapters 1-19 and 21-23 should also be followed, where applicable.

20.2.3. National and international requirements should be complied with. Requirements of the port where cargo operations take place should also be complied with and should be made known to seafarers, as appropriate.

20.2.4. Cargo handling equipment should be operated only by trained[1] and experienced persons. Manufacturer's instructions regarding operation and maintenance as contained in the ship's cargo handling manual[2] should be followed at all times.

20.2.5. Equipment should be inspected by a responsible officer prior to and after use. No equipment should be used or operated unless the prescribed certificates of tests and examinations are on the ship and are current and valid.

20.2.6. The officer with primary responsibility for cargo operations should check that all safety features are in place and that any possible hazards are clearly marked and otherwise dealt with to prevent injury to any persons who may be working on board the vessel.

20.2.7. The master and ship's officers should ensure that the crew is aware of any hazardous cargoes or operations. Appropriate

---

[1] At a minimum, in accordance with the STCW Convention, 1978, or any subsequent revision. Reference should be made to section 16 of the *IMO/ILO Document for guidance*.

[2] Guidance should also be obtained from the IMO's *Code of Safe Practice for Cargo Stowage and Securing*.

protective equipment should be provided to seafarers before commencement of cargo operations.

20.2.8. Prior to commencement of cargo operations, clear means and lines of communication should be established between the ship's crew and terminal personnel or dockworkers. This is particularly important in the case of hazardous cargoes or hazardous operations. If hand signals are to be used, their meaning must be clear to all those concerned in the operation.

20.2.9. All seafarers must take particular care to not exceed the safe working load of any equipment. The master and officers should take particular care, especially in older vessels, not to overstress any part of the ship's structure.

20.2.10. When work is interrupted or has temporarily ceased, hatches should be left in a safe condition, with either guard-rails or the hatch covers in position.

20.2.11. No other work should be carried out in a space in which cargo is being worked.

20.2.12. Seafarers should immediately report the damage of cargo handling equipment to a responsible ship's officer. Damaged equipment should be immediately taken out of service. Seafarers should never attempt to conceal damage to equipment from the responsible ship's officer or from dockworkers and others who may use the equipment.

20.2.13. When dangerous goods are carried, the guidance provided in Chapter 7 should be strictly followed.

20.2.14. Cargo gear should be properly stowed to prevent it from breaking loose and posing a hazard when the vessel is at sea.

20.2.15. Cargo should be stowed and secured assuming the worst weather conditions which may be expected.

20.2.16. When deck cargoes are carried, particularly timber,[1] attention should be paid to ensuring the ship's stability throughout the voyage, especially in consideration of the possibility of added weight due to absorption of water or accumulation of ice or snow.

20.3. Lifting gear

20.3.1. All lifting equipment used on board ship should be of good design, sound construction and material, adequate strength for the purpose for which it is used, free from defect, properly installed or assembled and properly maintained.

20.3.2. Lifting gear should be tested and examined in accordance with national requirements.

20.3.3. Lifting gear should be clearly and legibly marked with its safe working load, including the safe working load at various operating positions.

20.3.4. A register of a ship's lifting appliances and items of loose gear should be kept on the ship. All lifting gear and loose gear should be included in the register.[2]

20.3.5. All equipment should be thoroughly examined by a responsible officer before use and regularly examined during use. The frequency of examination should depend on the operation, e.g. derrick wires subjected to hard usage should be inspected several times a day.

---

[1] The IMO's *Code of Safe Practice for Ships Carrying Timber Deck Cargoes* should be consulted for carriage of timber.

[2] As provided in particular in the ILO *Code of Practice on Safety and Health in Dock Work*. Reference should also be made to Article 25(2) of the Safety and Health in Dock Work Convention, 1979 (No. 152).

20.3.6. Seafarers using cranes, derricks or special lifting gear should preferably be trained and certified for the particular equipment; if this is not possible, they should be thoroughly instructed by a competent ship's officer prior to any cargo operations.

20.3.7. Loads being lowered or hoisted should not pass or remain over any person engaged in loading or unloading or performing any other work in the vicinity.

20.3.8. Cargo handling equipment should always be manned when controls are in the "on" position. When not in operation it should be turned "off" and safety locks or devices should be put in place.

20.3.9. Persons operating equipment should have a clear view. If this is not possible, a signaller should be placed at a point clearly visible to the equipment operator and from the area of work.

20.4. Use of slings

20.4.1. Straps and slings should be of sufficient size and length to enable them to be used safely and be applied and pulled sufficiently tight to prevent the load or any part of the load from slipping and falling.

20.4.2. Before heavy loads such as lengths of steel sections, tubes and lumber are swung, the load should be given a trial lift to test the effectiveness of the slinging.

20.4.3. Except for the purpose of breaking out or making up slings, lifting hooks should not be attached to:

(a) the bands, straps or other fastenings of packages of cargo;

(b) the rims of barrels or drums.

20.4.4. Slings or chains being returned to the loading position should be securely hooked on the cargo hook before the signaller gives the signal to hoist. Hooks or claws should be attached to the egg link or shackle of the cargo hook and not allowed to hang loose. The cargo hook should be kept high enough to keep slings or chains clear of persons and obstructions.

20.4.5. Loads (setts) should be properly put together and properly slung before they are hoisted or lowered.

20.4.6. Loads should be raised and lowered smoothly, avoiding sudden jerks or "snatching" loads.

20.4.7. Suitable precautions, such as the use of packing or chafing pieces, should be taken to prevent chains, wire and fibre ropes from being damaged by the sharp edges of loads.

20.4.8. When slings are used with barrel hooks or similar holding devices where the weight of the load holds the hooks in place, the sling should be led down through the egg or eye link and through the eye of each hook in turn so that the horizontal part of the sling draws the hooks together.

20.4.9. The angle between the legs of slings should not normally exceed 90 degrees. Where this is not reasonably practicable, the angle may be exceeded up to 120 degrees provided that the slings have been designed to work at the greater angles.

20.4.10. Trays and pallets should be hoisted with four-legged slings and, where necessary, nets or other means should be used to prevent any part of the load falling.

20.4.11. When bundles of long metal goods such as tubes, pipes and rails are being hoisted, two slings should be used and, where necessary, a spreader. A suitable lanyard should also be attached, where necessary.

20.4.12. Cargo buckets, tubs and similar appliances should be carefully filled so that there is no risk of the contents falling out. They should be securely attached to the hoist (for example, by a shackle) to prevent tipping and displacement during hoisting and lowering.

20.4.13. Shackles should be used for slinging thick sheet metal if there are suitable holes in the material; otherwise, suitable clamps on an endless sling should be used.

20.4.14. Bricks and other loose goods of similar shape, carboys, small drums, canisters, etc., should be loaded or discharged in suitable boxes or pallets with sufficiently high sides and lifted by four-legged slings.

20.5. Pulley blocks

20.5.1. All blocks should be inspected before use and no block should be used unless it has identification marks and its safe working load marked on it in tonnes.

20.5.2. When a block is inspected it should be ascertained that no sheave is cracked, that it turns freely and the groove is not excessively worn, that the swivel head fitting is securely fastened and the block shank freely turns, that the side straps are sound and that all sheave clearances are satisfactory.

20.5.3. All grease nipples and/or lubrication holes should be kept clear and each block should be regularly greased.

20.6. Hooks

20.6.1. Every hook should be provided with an efficient device to prevent displacement of the sling or load or be of such construction as to prevent displacement.

20.6.2. Hooks should be marked with their safe working load.

20.7. Shackles

20.7.1. No shackle should be used unless its safe working load is clearly marked.

20.7.2. A shackle should be of the correct type, size and safe working load for its intended use.

20.7.3. All shackles should have their pins effectively secured or seized with wire.

20.7.4. The running part of any rigging should not come into contact with the pin of a shackle.

20.7.5. All shackle pins should be kept lubricated.

20.8. Working on deck while ship is at sea

20.8.1. The responsible officer should ensure that seafarers working on deck are properly instructed in the tasks which they are required to perform.

20.8.2. Seafarers should be prohibited at all times from sitting upon the vessel's bulwark or rail.

20.8.3. Bridge watchkeeping officers should be informed of all work being performed on deck or in deck spaces.

20.9. Heavy weather

20.9.1. Lifelines should be rigged in appropriate locations on deck if heavy weather is expected.

20.9.2. Attention should be given to the dangers of allowing any person out on deck during heavy weather.

20.9.3. No seafarers should be on deck during heavy weather unless it is absolutely necessary for the safety of the ship or crew.

20.9.4. The lashings of all deck cargo should be inspected and tightened as necessary when heavy weather is expected. Work on deck during heavy weather should be authorized by the master and the bridge watch should be informed.

20.9.5. Any person required to go on deck during heavy weather should wear a life-jacket and be equipped with a portable transceiver. If possible, the person should remain in communication with a back-up person and be visible at all times.

20.9.6. Seafarers on deck should wear reflective clothing.

20.9.7. Seafarers should work in pairs or in teams. All seafarers should be under the command of an experienced senior officer.

20.10. Working in hatches and holds

20.10.1. Reference should be made to Chapters 8, 9 and 10.

20.10.2. Before any work in any hatches or holds where the atmosphere may contain toxic or flammable gases or be deficient in oxygen, the enclosed-space procedures outlined in Chapter 10 should be observed.

20.10.3. If work is to be performed on or near a tall stack of cargo, an officer should ensure that it is safe to do so. Safety nets should be rigged where appropriate.

20.10.4. When possible, loosely stowed dunnage should not be walked upon. If this is unavoidable, care should be taken not to walk on any protruding nails.

20.10.5. Work should not be carried out in holds where cargo operations are taking place.

21. Working in machinery spaces

21.1. General provisions

21.1.1. All operations in machinery spaces should be performed by a competent person under the supervision of a responsible officer or senior rating.[1]

21.1.2. The regulations of the competent authority on the guarding of every dangerous part of a vessel's machinery should apply (see also Chapter 13).

21.1.3. Reference should be made to Chapter 5 concerning protective equipment. Particular attention should be paid to protecting seafarers from the effects of noise.[2] Spaces in which hearing protection needs to be worn should be indicated by warning signs.

21.1.4. No work other than routine duties should be undertaken except on the orders of a responsible engineering officer. Maintenance work should be carried out in compliance with manufacturer's instruction manuals. When necessary, specific work should be carried out within the "permit-to-work" system (see Chapter 4).

21.1.5. Moving parts of machinery should be provided with permanent guards or other safety devices such as railings or fencing.

---

[1] At a minimum, in accordance with the STCW Regulations, Chapter III or any subsequent revision. Reference should be made to sections 20-25 of the *IMO/ILO Document for Guidance*.

[2] See also the Guarding of Machinery Convention, 1963 (No. 119), and the Working Environment (Air Pollution, Noise and Vibration) Convention, 1977 (No. 148). Further guidance may be obtained from the ILO *Code of Practice on Protection of Workers against Noise and Vibration in the Working Environment* (Geneva, 1984).

21.1.6. If the use of any piece of machinery or equipment is considered to be temporarily unsafe, it should be immobilized or put in a safe place or condition immediately and, if necessary, a warning notice should be posted adjacent to or at the control position.

21.1.7. No guard, fencing or shielding should be removed for repair or maintenance except when the machinery to which it relates has been stopped. The machinery should not be restarted until the fencing or shielding has been replaced and secured.

21.1.8. All valves, pipes and fittings should be adequately supported and fixed or clamped to avoid vibration and possible fracture. All such fixtures and supports should be properly maintained and replaced after maintenance.

21.1.9. All items such as steam pipes, exhaust pipes and fittings which, because of their location and operating temperature present a hazard, should be adequately lagged or shielded.

21.1.10. The source of any oil leak should be located as soon as possible and the leak stopped.

21.1.11. Waste oil should not be allowed to accumulate in the bilges or on tank tops. Any accumulation should be removed as soon as possible in compliance with MARPOL.[1] Tank top and bilge spaces should be washed down at regular intervals or as necessary for safety.

21.1.12. A procedure should be in place to ensure that, whenever a fuel oil tank is being filled, or the contents of one are being transferred to another, it does not overflow. Such a procedure may be in writing and may include permanently displayed line diagrams and particulars. Whenever fuel oil is being loaded or transferred, the operation should be supervised by a competent person.

---

[1] MARPOL, Annex I.

21.1.13. Bilges and mud-boxes should be kept clear of rubbish and other substances so that the bilges can be easily pumped.

21.1.14. Special attention should be given to preventing leakages into machinery spaces of exhaust gases from boilers, inert gas plants, uptakes, etc.

21.1.15. (1) All areas should be suitably illuminated. Areas under floor plates where oil pipes are located should be painted a light colour.

(2) Any light that fails should be replaced as soon as possible.

(3) Temporary or portable lighting should be used to provide additional illumination as required, and should be removed immediately after use.

21.1.16. Care should be taken to keep the noise level as low as practicable, and to maintain or where necessary improve sound-absorbing arrangements.

21.1.17. Seafarers should be informed of the danger of removing hearing protection in areas where the noise level is high, even for short periods. When work has to be carried out in such areas, a suitable system of communication should be agreed upon before the work begins.

21.1.18. If there is a control room, doors should be kept closed and hearing protection should be worn when access is required to any area where the noise level is high.

21.1.19. (1) Ventilation should be maintained to ensure a comfortable atmosphere so far as is reasonably practicable in all areas, with special attention being given to working areas and control rooms.

(2) Ventilation should be increased if necessary where maintenance and repair work have to be carried out in areas of high temperature or high humidity.

21.1.20. Unless properly equipped and authorized to be operated without persons in attendance, the boiler room and machinery space should be under the direct supervision of a competent person at all times and should be manned at all times by persons adequate for the duties required.

21.1.21. (1) All drains on such equipment as pipes and filters should be kept clear.

(2) Care should be taken to ensure that any pressure in all relevant piping, system or container has been relieved before it is opened or any flange or joint is broken.

(3) As a precaution bolts should be only slackened back and not removed until the flange or joint is broken.

(4) If the flange or joint does not part easily, separation should be made with a wedge and not by allowing pressure into the line. The pipe should be secured temporarily if necessary before the flange or joint is broken.

(5) It should be remembered that valves may not be completely tight nor lines fully drained and that pressure, or accumulations of oil and scalding water, may build up in a pipe even after the pressure has been relieved.

(6) Any valve controlling flow should be effectively locked or secured as long as the line remains open, and if necessary a warning notice should be posted.

21.1.22. All stores and tools should be properly stowed and adequate arrangements should be made, particularly with heavy stores, to secure each item in heavy weather.

21.1.23. When lifting weights, seafarers should avoid strains by using chainblocks or the engine room crane, as appropriate. When turning valves or handwheels, seafarers should avoid strains by using lever or wheel spanners.

21.1.24. (1) Where heavy items are lifted by chainblocks or by an engine room crane, the lifting device and lifting arrangements should be examined by a responsible person, who should ensure that the safe working load is not exceeded.

(2) Slings should be examined for broken or ragged stands, and padded as required to avoid damage on sharp edges.

21.1.25. (1) Where lifting or eye bolts are to be used, the thread on the bolt and in the part to be lifted should be seen to be clean and in good condition, and the threaded part fully screwed home and locked as appropriate before any lifting effort is applied.

(2) This is particularly important when lifting heavy machinery parts, when care should be taken that carbon is removed from the threaded recess, if necessary by running down the appropriate tap before screwing home the bolt.

(3) Hoisting or lowering, whether by crane or by chainblocks, should be performed only after all persons involved have been informed of the intended action.

21.1.26. Any friction fit, tightness or adhesion of the part of any load being lifted should be broken by wedges or tapping, and not by increasing the load on the lifting appliance.

21.1.27. Seafarers should always stand clear of any load being lifted and should not walk close to or underneath any load being lifted or while it is suspended.

21.1.28. (1) Any tools used at heights above platform level should be kept in a suitable bag or box, or secured so as to prevent them from falling.

(2) After any repair or maintenance work, all tools and any spares or replaced parts should be checked, accounted for and properly stowed away in a safe and secure place.

21.1.29. When working alone, a person should arrange to communicate at regular and frequent intervals with other persons in the machinery spaces or on the bridge.

21.2. Boilers, unfired pressure vessels and steam pipes

21.2.1. No person should perform any operation on a boiler, unfired pressure vessel or steam pipe that could result in the release of steam, air, or oil except:

(a)   under the supervision of an engineer officer; and

(b)   with the knowledge and approval of the chief engineer.

21.2.2. All boilers and unfired pressure vessels and steam piping should be inspected internally and externally at regular intervals by a competent person as required by the national authority.

21.2.3. No boiler or unfired pressure vessel should be operated or kept at working pressure if unsafe for use or not provided with the properly maintained fittings necessary for safe operation.

21.2.4. (1) Before any boiler or unfired pressure vessel is opened for inspection, any pressure therein should be released, the contents cooled down to atmospheric temperature and the system effectively drained off.

(2) No boiler or unfired pressure vessel should be opened or entered for inspection until adequate arrangements have been made to prevent any backflow of steam or working fluid by blanking off, or locking shut, any lines or valves that might allow such backflow of steam, hot water or exhaust gases to enter the boilers, combustion chamber or pressure vessel.

(3) The top manhole door should be knocked in first with the dogs slacked back but not removed.

(4) The manhole door should be held by a rope or other means when the dogs are removed.

(5) When the top manhole has been removed, the bottom manhole door may be knocked in.

(6) At all times while a person is in the boiler, another person should be standing by at the manhole entrance and should communicate at frequent intervals with the person inside.

21.2.5. Spaces at the top and sides of boilers should not be used for storage.

21.2.6. Safety valves should be properly sealed and maintained in good operational condition at all times.

21.2.7. Special care should be taken to maintain water gauges in proper order. They should be checked and blown through in a proper manner by a competent person at frequent intervals. Gauges should be replaced only by a competent person.

21.2.8. The water level should be checked at all times when fires are alight. Should the water level fall below the glass, the boiler should be immediately secured as required.

21.2.9. (1) Care should be taken to ensure that, when lighting up, the combustion chambers have been properly purged free of gas and that no loose oil has accumulated on the furnace floor.

(2) Care should be taken to ascertain that all burners are clean and properly assembled.

(3) Fuel oil should be recirculated until all parts of the system have reached a suitable temperature before admission to the furnace.

(4) When lighting up a boiler, seafarers should stand clear of any openings in order to avoid a possible blowback.

21.2.10. Should a furnace fail to light for any reason when the oil valve is opened:

(a)   the valve should be closed;

(b)   the combustion chamber should be properly purged.

21.2.11 Operating instructions should be displayed at each boiler.

21.3. Propulsion machinery

21.3.1. The propulsion machinery should be provided and maintained in accordance with the requirements of the competent authority and good practice.

21.3.2. Maintenance should be carried out by a competent person and a responsible officer should be informed immediately if any actual, or latent, fault or defect is observed, with remedial action being taken as appropriate.

21.3.3. The machinery should be stopped before any work is done by seafarers on, or using, machinery items which would constitute a hazard:

(a) throttle or starting system should be closed;

(b) turning gear or a suitable brake should be engaged; and

(c) a warning notice should be posted.

21.4. Turbines

21.4.1. The governor, low lubricating oil pressure alarm and shutdown devices, and other speed limiting devices should be made ready to operate should abnormal operations occur.

21.4.2. Steam joints, valve gland and gland sealing arrangements should be maintained in good order to avoid excessively high humidity in the surrounding area.

21.5. Internal combustion engines

21.5.1. Internal combustion machinery should be maintained in safe condition and be regularly inspected as required by the manufacturer.

21.5.2. Scavenge trunks should be kept clean and free from loose oil and turbo-blowers should be kept free of accumulations of oil and dirt.

21.5.3. A source of ignition, e.g. a portable electric light or naked flame, should not be brought near an open engine crank case until it has been cooled and well ventilated and until all explosive gases have been expelled.

21.6. Air compressors and reservoirs

21.6.1. Air compressors should be properly maintained an inspected by a competent officer.

21.7. Refrigeration systems

21.7.1. Adequate information stating the operating and maintenance safeguards of the refrigeration plant should be displayed on each vessel.

21.7.2. Refrigeration compressors and systems should be properly maintained to avoid leakage of refrigerant, either in the compressor room or in the refrigerated compartments. Where refrigerating equipment is isolated, a competent person should be notified before entering the room or compartment.

21.7.3. When leakage is suspected the proper detection method should be used.

21.7.4. No one should enter a refrigerated compartment without wearing protective clothing and informing a responsible person.

21.8. Oil-based systems

21.8.1. Special precautions should be taken when working on systems containing oil and, in particular, hot oil.

21.8.2. All protective covers on oil lines should be drained before removing same. Protective covers should be promptly replaced after completion of any work and after verification that no leaks are evident in the system.

21.8.3. Attention is drawn to the potential fire hazard associated with the rupture of unprotected oil lines and joints.

21.8.4. Safety devices of oil pumps, oil heaters and coolers should be maintained in good and operative condition.

21.9. Steering gear

21.9.1. The operation of the steering gear should be checked or inspected at frequent intervals by the responsible officer and safety devices should be ready to operate at all times.

21.9.2. The steering gear should be tested in accordance with IMO requirements.[1]

21.10. Control-room operation and unattended machinery spaces

21.10.1. Only authorized persons should enter a control room or an unattended machinery space.

---

[1] SOLAS, 1974, Chapter V, Regulations 19-1 and 19-2, as amended.

21.10.2. Seafarers should never enter, or remain in, an unattended machinery space unless permission has been received from, or instructions given by, the engineer officer in charge at the time.

21.10.3. When watchkeeping is carried out from a control room, the competent person should ensure that the machinery space is patrolled at regular intervals by a person sufficiently knowledgeable to detect any unusual conditions.

21.10.4. The instrumentation and alarms on which the safety of an unattended installation depends should be maintained in good operational order in accordance with the manufacturer's instructions.

21.10.5. Unmanned machinery spaces should be properly lit at all times.

21.10.6. (1) Any alarms that have operated should be made reoperative before the machinery space is left.

(2) No alarm system should be isolated without the permission of the chief engineer.

21.10.7. At any time when the machinery spaces are to be left unattended, a responsible officer should ensure that all alarm systems are set to operate and that all persons have been accounted for and have left the space.

21.10.8. Should the responsible officer enter the space alone for any reason, he should notify the bridge duty officer who should arrange to check on his well-being frequently and at specific times as long as he remains therein.[1]

21.10.9. Notices of safety precautions to be observed by seafarers working in control-rooms and unattended machinery spaces should be clearly displayed at entrances.

---

[1] STCW, 1978, Annex-Regulations, Chapter III, Engine Department, or subsequent revisions.

21.11. Hydraulic systems

21.11.1. Hydraulic systems should be frequently inspected by a responsible officer, properly maintained and kept free of leaks.

21.11.2. Care should be taken to avoid skin penetration from high pressure fluid during inspections and repair of hydraulic systems.

21.11.3. The system should be purged as necessary to avoid erratic operations which could be dangerous to seafarers.

22. Working in galleys, pantries and other food handling areas[1]

22.1. Loading and storing provisions

22.1.1. All seafarers working in the galley, pantry and other food handling areas should be trained in related safety measures before assuming their responsibilities.

22.1.2. (1) Whenever possible stores and provisions should be taken aboard, preferably by a crane or derrick, onto a deck area where no cargo is being worked.

(2) There should be a short and convenient route to the storerooms. As far as practicable this route should not pass across areas where cargo is being worked.

22.1.3. (1) Care should be taken to ensure that any obstructions between the loading area and the storerooms are marked or properly protected.

(2) Where possible, wooden ramps should be installed so as to provide unimpeded passage over steps or obstructions.

22.1.4. When crates are handled or opened, any protruding nails or staples should be removed and crates or chests should be made safe and any metal strips or projections removed before handling.

22.1.5. Any hooks or sharp equipment used for handling stores should be stowed in a safe place.

---

[1] See also the Food and Catering (Ships' Crews) Convention, 1946 (No. 68).

22.1.6. (1) Refrigerator chamber doors should be fitted with:

(a) a device of adequate strength to hold them open in a seaway; and

(b) a means of opening them from the inside.

(2) Refrigerator rooms should have a means of sounding the alarm both from inside and outside.

(3) The area immediately outside should have a slip-resistant surface.

22.1.7. If a leakage of refrigerant in a refrigerated storage space is suspected:

(a) a warning notice to that effect should be posted on the door or access; and

(b) seafarers should not enter.

22.1.8. (1) When seafarers enter refrigerated chambers that are usually padlocked they should take the padlocks in with them.

(2) Seafarers should make themselves familiar with the operation of the inside release for the door and the location of the alarm button so they may be easily found in the dark.

22.1.9. The proper functioning of alarm bells, door clasps and the inside release should be checked at regular intervals.

22.2. Preparation of food

22.2.1. Extra caution should be taken in all catering operations when the vessel is moving in a seaway.

22.2.2. (1) When meat is being chopped, special care should be taken to ensure that:

(a) the chopping block is firm;

(b) the cutting area of the meat is well on the block;

(c) fingers, arms and legs are clear of the line of strike; and

(d) protective gloves are worn.

(2) Chopping blocks should be placed in a clear unobstructed area so as to reduce any danger to the seafarer concerned to a minimum and to eliminate dangers to others nearby.

22.2.3. (1) When foodstuffs are being chopped or cut with a knife, fingers should be bent inwards towards the palm of the hand with the thumb overlapped by the forefinger.

(2) The knife should be angled away from the work so that the blade is sloped away from the fingers as the work is fed to the knife.

22.2.4. (1) When meat is being sawed or boned, care should be taken to ensure that the saw or knife does not slip off the bone. A protective apron should be worn.

(2) Cutting should be done with smooth, firm strokes, care being taken to keep the fingers clear of the cutting edge.

22.2.5. (1) All cuts, however small, should be reported immediately and treated for infection.

(2) They should be covered by a waterproof dressing when food is being handled.

22.2.6. Adequate lighting should be provided where catering operations are carried out, with additional lighting as necessary in areas where cutting or chopping is done.

22.2.7. All areas where catering operations are carried out should be adequately ventilated. Cooking areas should be provided with exhaust ventilation. The uptakes and any filters in such a system should be cleaned at frequent intervals to remove oily deposits.

22.2.8. Hot pots and pans should not be full, since they may overflow in a seaway.

22.2.9. Care should be taken never to leave pans or fat unattended in an oven or on a heating stove, nor to allow water to come into contact with hot fat.

22.2.10. (1) All seafarers working in the galley should be trained in the use of appropriate fire-fighting equipment, including the use of a smothering blanket and appropriate type of fire extinguisher.

(2) Water should never be used to extinguish burning fat.

22.2.11. Broken glass or crockery should be cleaned up immediately using a brush and pan.

22.2.12. (1) Seafarers working in catering operations should wear clean clothing, particularly when handling food and preparing meals, and should wash hands and clean finger nails before handling food and after using the toilet.

(2) A supply of clean, hot running water, soap and clean towels should be available.

22.2.13. Sea water taps should preferably not be fitted in the galley. Sea water should never be used in the preparation of food.

22.2.14. Particularly when purchased in a hot climate, vegetables to be used in salads should always be thoroughly washed in clean running fresh water before being served. Fruit should preferably be washed and peeled before being eaten.

22.2.15. (1) Seafarers should not be permitted to handle food or cooking utensils, etc., when suffering from dysentery, diarrhoea or stomach disorders of an infectious nature.

(2) They should report any such complaints, spots or rashes to a competent officer at the earliest opportunity.

22.2.16. All accommodation areas and particularly places where food is stored or prepared should be inspected regularly to ensure cleanliness and freedom from insects, mice and rats.

22.2.17. (1) Absolute cleanliness should be maintained in respect of food, crockery, cutlery, cooking utensils and stores.

(2) Clean clothes should always be worn in pantries, saloons and mess rooms.

(3) Cracked or chipped crockery and glassware should be discarded.

(4) Any food which has been in contact with broken glass or crockery should be thrown out.

22.2.18. Smoking should be prohibited in kitchens, galleys, pantries, storerooms or other places where food is stored, handled or prepared and notices to this effect should be displayed.

22.2.19. (1) Cleaning and washing substances should be used only for the purpose intended and never in excess of the quantities recommended in the manufacturer's instructions.

(2) Protective gloves should be worn, particularly when handling concentrated liquids.

(3) Care should be taken to prevent concentrated liquids and powders from coming in contact with exposed areas of the skin or eyes. In the event of exposure, the affected area should be immediately washed with copious amounts of fresh water and an eye flushing device used where necessary.

(4) The seafarer should report the incident quickly to the competent person.

22.3. Work in galleys, pantries and serving food

22.3.1. (1) Care should be taken to avoid tripping and slipping when moving around galleys or carrying or serving food.

(2) Decks should be kept free of grease or rubbish, and if any oil or grease is spilt, the person responsible should clean it up im-

mediately or see that others are warned of the risk until the cleaning up is completed.

22.3.2. Seafarers should be particularly careful when carrying food and using stairs and companionways, which should be kept clear and unobstructed. In particular, one hand should be kept free to hold handrails or supports. Loads should be carried in such a manner as not to obstruct the line of view, and movements should not be hurried.

22.3.3. Suitable protective footwear of a type that fully covers the foot, with slip-resistant soles, should be worn at all times.

22.3.4. (1) Seafarers should be careful to avoid burns and scalding when handling hot pans and dishes, removing lids off boilers, opening steamers and pressure cookers, immersing the hands in hot water in the sinks or opening oven doors.

(2) Clean dry cloths should be used for picking up utensils too hot to handle.

22.3.5. (1) Before washing down the galley, electrical appliances should be unplugged or otherwise isolated from the power source and stoves should be switched off. There should be no form of hot oil on stove tops and other similarly exposed locations where they may be subject to splashing.

(2) Decks should be mopped clear and surplus water removed after washing.

(3) Skylights and other openings to the deck should be arranged so as to prevent rain or spray from entering the galley.

22.3.6. (1) Any defects in equipment or utensils should be reported to the responsible officer, who should arrange for their repair or replacement as soon as possible.

(2) The defective item should be taken out of service.

(3) Unauthorized seafarers should never attempt to repair oil-fired or electrical ranges or equipment.

22.3.7. The potentially dangerous heated or moving parts of any machinery or equipment used in the catering department should have suitable guards, which should always be in position when being used or operated.

22.3.8. (1) Seafarers should be trained and properly instructed:

(a) in the use of any mechanical or electrical equipment which they may be required to use or operate; and

(b) in the dangers of cutting instruments and slicing, mincing and chopping machines.

(2) Such equipment should not usually be used by young persons unless they have been properly instructed and are supervised.

22.3.9. (1) Personnel should ensure that all safety devices are in place before operating such machines, and should use them in a proper manner.

(2) Cleaning should never be carried out when any part is in motion, and the power should be disconnected from any electrical equipment before cleaning any part or removing any blockage.

(3) When a user is in doubt as to the operation of any electrically driven machine, the machine should be switched off and a responsible person informed.

22.3.10. (1) Sharp knives, saws and choppers should be safely stowed in a proper rack.

(2) They should not be left lying around or in washing-up water.

(3) Tins should be opened only with proper tin openers, which should preferably be securely mounted on a bench or bulkhead.

22.3.11. (1) Seafarers should always follow printed instructions when lighting up oil-fired ovens or stoves.

(2) The interior should be inspected to ensure that no oil is lying in the bottom.

(3) Air should be blown through to clear any gas.

(4) The special torch provided should be lit and inserted before the oil is turned on.

(5) No other means of lighting should ever be used.

(6) The face and body should be kept well clear of the burner aperture during the lighting operation.

22.3.12. (1) Should the burner fail to light:

(a)   the oil should be turned off; and

(b)   air should be blown through the furnace for two or three minutes to clear any oil vapour before an attempt is made to relight the burner.

(2) Seafarers should never attempt to relight a burner from the hot brickwork of the furnace, but should always follow the printed instructions.

23. Safety in living accommodation[1]

23.1. General provisions

23.1.1. Cabins and accommodation should be kept in a clean and tidy condition. Shipowners should provide the necessary cleaning equipment for this purpose.

23.1.2. The emergency stations and duties of the occupants of each cabin should be clearly displayed in that cabin or immediately adjacent to the door of the cabin. Seafarers should read and memorize this information immediately upon being allocated the cabin.

23.1.3. Towels and clothing should be put away in their proper place when not in use. Wet clothing should be hung in drying rooms and be kept clear of light bulbs, radiators and other sources of heat.

23.1.4. (1) After smoking, personnel should take care to ensure that all butts and ashes are properly extinguished. Seafarers should never smoke in bed.

(2) When personal electrical equipment is used, it should be checked by a competent person.

(3) Multi-outlet plugs should not be used.

(4) Disposable fuses should never be rewired or replaced by others of a higher rating.

(5) Portable lamps, radios and other electrical equipment should be switched off at the main switch when not in use or when the user

---

[1] See also the Accommodation of Crew Convention (Revised), 1949 (No. 92), the Accommodation of Crews (Supplementary Provisions) Convention, 1970 (No. 133), the Crew Accommodation (Air Conditioning) Recommendation, 1970 (No. 140), the Crew Accommodation (Noise Control) Recommendation, 1970 (No. 141), and the IMO Code on Noise Levels on Board Ships (Resolution No. A.468(XII)).

leaves the room. They should be properly secured against movement.

(6) Faulty wiring should be immediately reported to a competent person.

23.1.5. Slip-resistant bath mats and proper handholds should be provided in bathrooms and showers.

23.1.6. Seafarers should recognize that the safety of individuals and of the entire ship and crew depends upon off-duty crew members being able to get adequate rest and sleep. Noise and other behaviour which may disturb others should be kept to a minimum.[1]

23.1.7. Before leaving a common space, seafarers should always check that chairs and other loose objects are appropriately secured against movement.

23.1.8. Accommodation areas should be inspected as part of a fire patrol when most seafarers are asleep.

23.2. Laundering appliances

23.2.1. The manufacturer's operating instructions for washing, cleaning or drying machines should be followed.

23.2.2. Clothes washing and drying machines should be installed according to the manufacturer's instructions concerning ventilation and operation.

23.2.3. When hand or industrial irons are used, precautions should be taken to avoid burns and scalds and such equipment should be switched off and returned to the stowed position whenever the user leaves the laundry room.

---

[1] ILO Recommendation No. 141.

23.2.4. Any malfunction or damage to the equipment should be reported to a responsible person.

23.2.5. The precautions described in Chapter 17 should be taken when dry-cleaning chemicals are used.

23.3. Physical fitness rooms

23.3.1. All equipment should be installed and used in accordance with the manufacturer's instruction.

23.3.2. Seafarers should be encouraged to use the equipment to maintain health and fitness.

23.4. Swimming-pools

23.4.1. When a swimming pool is available, seafarers should take precautions against the ordinary risks of swimming and diving. Warning signs should be placed around the pool to discourage dangerous activities such as swimming alone or diving.

23.4.2. The swimming-pool should be emptied when heavy weather is expected.

23.4.3. The water in the swimming-pool should be changed at regular intervals and the pool should not be filled with water which might be injurious to health.

23.5. Sewage systems

23.5.1. The dangers of gases from sewages systems being generated and finding their way into working and living spaces and the importance of the hazards these present should be brought to the attention of all seafarers. An operational procedure should be introduced for reporting and recording inspections and maintenance of the sewage system and the action taken to deal with complaints of foul or musty smells which may be due to toxic or oxygen-depleted gases.

23.5.2. The use of toilet cleaning products which kill germs and bacteria should be avoided as they may destroy the bacteria which are essential to the aerobic operation of sewage treatment plants. The manufacturer of the treatment plant should be consulted for details of appropriate non-harmful cleaning products.

23.5.3. If entry into the sewage tanks or work on the system is necessary, all personnel engaged on this work should be informed of the hazards of encountering oxygen-depleted, toxic and flammable gases (see Chapter 10).

23.5.4. The following should be checked:

(a) that all drainpipes have satisfactory water/gas tightness and adequate water seals and traps to prevent backflow of gases into the respective compartments;

(b) that all sanitary fittings are securely fastened to prevent relative movements at pipe joints;

(c) that where toilet pans are fitted with vacuum-breaking arrangements at the back of the water trap, such as individual air pipes or patented backflow prevention valves, these are in a satisfactory condition and operation;

(d) that there is an adequate supply of flush water to clear toilet pans and to replenish water seals.

23.5.5. It should be made certain that drains and air vents are clear of obstruction and are in sound water/gas tight condition throughout their length. Adequate air vents should be fitted to the piping network, paying special attention to the extremities of the system. These should ensure an adequate supply of air and prevent plugs of water from breaking the water seal during violent rolling or pitching.

23.5.6. Ventilation systems to all compartments of a ship should be designed, installed and balanced to ensure satisfactory distribution of air. They should be maintained in a clean and efficient condition to achieve the designed air changes throughout the service life of the vessel. Particular attention should be paid to the exhaust or extraction systems in toilet or washing areas. In general, attention should be paid to the examination of extraction grilles, louvres, ducts, etc., to ensure that they are clear and free of accumulated dirt, fluff, etc.

24. Specific vessel types

24.1. General provisions

24.1.1. Reference should be made to Chapters 1-23 where applicable.

24.1.2. The appropriate national and international requirements should be observed.

24.1.3. In all operations maintaining a high level of safety should be the first priority. The operations and the hazards should be thoroughly explained to seafarers carrying out their respective tasks and the safety precautions for each task should be fully understood. In particular:

(a) where there is a high risk from fire and explosion rules restricting smoking and the carriage of matches and cigarette lighters must be observed. Smoking should not be permitted on board except in places and at times permitted by the master;

(b) spillages and leaks of hazardous substances, such as petroleum and some mineral oils, should be attended to immediately. The shipowner should provide seafarers with information and personal protective equipment for the safe handling of such spillages;

(c) oil-soaked rags and other materials present a fire hazard and may spontaneously ignite. They must be disposed of in compliance with MARPOL.[1] Other combustible rubbish should not be allowed to accumulate;

(d) cargo handling equipment, testing instruments, automatic and other alarm systems should be well maintained;

---

[1] MARPOL, Annexes I and V.

(e)   work which could cause sparking or which involves the use of heat should not be undertaken unless authorized and after the work area has been tested and found gas-free, or otherwise declared safe;

(f)   where work in an enclosed space is necessary, the guidance in Chapter 10 should be strictly followed;

(g)   "permit to work" procedures should be adopted unless the work presents no undue hazard (see Chapter 4);

(h)   appropriate personal protective equipment should be worn.

24.1.4.   Seafarers should be properly trained in accordance with applicable national and international requirements.[1] Training in emergency procedures and the use of any special emergency equipment should be undertaken at regular intervals. This should include medical first aid measures, in the event of accidental contact with harmful substances and inhalation of dangerous gases or fumes.

24.1.5.   Shipowners should provide the master and crew with adequate instructions and information on all operations. Those on board responsible for the safe loading and carriage of the cargo should also be provided with all the relevant information pertinent to the cargo before it is loaded and about the precautions to be taken during the voyage. The remainder of the crew should also be advised of any precautions they should take. At all loading and discharging ports a safety checklist should be reviewed by the master and an official from the marine terminal.[2] Before starting cargo loading, the stowage and loading procedure should be discussed and agreed between the master and the terminal operator.

---

[1] See the International Convention on Standards of Training, Certification and Watchkeeping for Seafarers (STCW), 1978, as amended or revised, as well as associated resolutions.

[2] An example is the Ship-Shore Checklist for Oil Tankers, contained in Appendix A of the Safety Guide for Oil Tankers and Terminals (ISGOTT) published by the International Chamber of Shipping.

24.1.6. Shipowners should ensure that all ships are equipped with the correct operational and loading manuals.

24.1.7. To minimize the risk of exposure to cargo which could irritate the skin, seafarers should wear appropriate protective clothing and use barrier creams. They should wash themselves and their clothing to remove residual cargo dust so that it is not carried into the living spaces and ingested accidentally while eating. This is particularly relevant for those materials identified as toxic in the IMDG Code.

24.1.8. At sea, lashings on deck, in cargo holds, in engine rooms or in stores, should be checked regularly and tightened if necessary. During heavy weather, where appropriate, the heading of the ship should be changed in order to facilitate the tightening of the lashings to reduce potential hazards.

24.2. Bulk carriers and carriage of bulk cargoes

24.2.1. The dust created by certain cargoes, particularly in loading, discharging or hold cleaning operations, may pose an explosion hazard and should be limited, as far as possible, to the minimum.

24.2.2. Many solid bulk cargoes,[1] some seemingly innocuous, can cause health problems for seafarers in various ways. For example:

(a) ammonium nitrate fertilizers produce toxic gases upon decomposition;

(b) antimony ore dust is toxic if inhaled;

(c) barium nitrate dust on food is toxic if swallowed;

(d) castor oil beans *(Ricinus communis)* when handled may cause severe irritation of the skin and eyes.

---

[1] Appendix B of the IMO's *Code of Safe Practice for Solid Bulk Cargoes* should be consulted.

24.2.3. Portholes, doors, etc., should be kept closed in port if they permit cargo dust to enter the ship's accommodation area.

24.2.4. Spaces used for the carriage of bulk cargoes should be treated as confined or dangerous spaces. The procedures for entering such spaces, set out in Chapter 10, should be strictly followed.

24.2.5. The properties of dry bulk cargoes should be carefully considered as certain bulk materials are liable to oxidation. This may result in oxygen reduction, emission of toxic fumes and self-heating. Other materials may emit toxic fumes, particularly when wet. Other materials, if they become wet, are corrosive to skin, eyes and mucous membranes, as well as to the ship's structure.

24.2.6. Ships which carry cargoes that may emit toxic gases, for whatever reason, should be provided with the appropriate gas detection equipment.

24.2.7. Many bulk cargoes, particularly ores, are loaded into holds from great heights and at very fast rates. This can create sufficient stress to damage the structure of the vessel. This could be avoided by reducing the loading rate.

24.2.8. The plans for the loading and discharging of ships should be properly adhered to, so that the vessel is not exposed to unacceptable stresses, shear forces and bending moments. Special consideration should be given to the dangers of overstress on large and older ships in particular, especially where alternative holds are loaded.

24.2.9. Some kinds of cargoes, including concentrates, certain coals and other materials with similar physical properties, may liquefy above the transportable moisture limit and cause a shift in cargo. The moisture content should therefore be carefully checked prior to loading and during the voyage, as moisture migration may occur due to vibration and/or ship motion.

24.2.10. (1) Precautions to prevent liquids entering cargo holds in which bulk cargoes are stowed should be maintained throughout the voyage.

(2) Precautions should be taken against sea water entering holds through hatch covers moving or flexing when the ship is working in a seaway.

(3) Water should not be used to cool cargoes which may liquefy.

24.2.11. The appropriate national and international requirements with respect to ventilation should be observed. Certain cargoes, such as some coals, copra, swarf, charcoal and concentrates, etc., are liable to spontaneous combustion if the temperature is high enough. Cooling such material should be carried out with extreme care since water used to cool the cargo may actually cause increased heating and may also lead to spontaneous combustion and/or explosion. The temperature of holds containing such cargo should be checked daily or in accordance with the shipowner's instructions.

24.2.12. The dust from some bulk cargoes including grain dust can be explosive. Particularly when cleaning holds after discharge, seafarers should be made aware of this hazard: smoking should be prohibited or restricted and cleaning carried out so as to minimize dust formation, for example, by hosing down.

24.2.13. Seafarers should not enter wing tanks when grain is being loaded.

24.3. Container ships

24.3.1. For general requirements with respect to these vessels, see 24.1.1 to 24.1.8.[1]

---

[1] For stowage and securing of containers on ships' decks not specifically designed and fitted for this purpose, reference should be made to Annex 1 of the IMO's *Code of Safe Practice for Cargo Stowage and Securing* (resolution A.714(17) adopted by the Assembly of the IMO at its 17th Session (1991)), or any subsequent revisions.

24.3.2. Seafarers should receive special training as required and in particular in the operation and maintenance of onboard container cranes where utilized.

24.3.3. Shipowners should provide each ship with instruction manuals for the operation and maintenance of cargo handling equipment. A stowing and securing manual should also be provided.

24.3.4. Each container should be fitted with a safety approval plate specifying the country of approval, date of manufacture, identification number, maximum operating gross weights, allowable stacking weight, transverse racking and test load value.[1]

24.3.5. The stack height of containers should take account of their design strength and also not impair visibility from the bridge.[2] The number of tiers on deck or in the hold should not exceed the design limitation.

24.3.6. When carrying containers on a hatch cover the strength of the hatch cover should not be exceeded. Covers should be restrained against sliding and tipping by approved type stoppers and locking devices.

24.3.7. Containers stowed on deck should be secured to the ship, for example, by stacking cones and twist locks. Twist locks can be used effectively when containers are stowed one or two high, especially if the container in the second tier is either light loaded or empty. Care should be taken that twist locks are placed in the correct way and locked. When the number of tiers on deck exceeds two, stacking cones and wire or steel rod lashings should be used.

---

[1] The International Convention for Safe Containers and the Marking of Weight (Packages Transported by Vessels) Convention, 1929 (No. 27), set out requirements for proper marking of weight.

[2] SOLAS, 1974, as amended.

24.3.8. All containers should be effectively secured, preferably at the bottom corners, in a way which will guard against sliding.

24.3.9. No restraint systems should be imposed on containers, or any of their fittings, which create forces in excess of those for which they have been designed.

24.3.10. Seafarers should wear personal protective equipment when carrying out cargo operations, fitting or securing deck lashings and should use specially designed leverage bars to tighten cargo tensioning devices.

24.3.11. In the handling of containers, attention should be paid to the possibility of uneven or poorly distributed loading or incorrectly declared weight.

24.3.12. Heavy items of machinery or plant which are stored on flats may need to be further secured by additional lashings.

24.3.13. Safe means should be provided for access to containers stacked on deck to check lashings, etc. Where appropriate, seafarers should be protected from falling by the use of a safety harness properly secured or by other suitable arrangements.

24.3.14. Where the ship's electrical supply is used for refrigerated containers, the supply cables should be provided with proper connection for the power circuits and for earthing the container. Before the supply is used, cables and connections should be inspected and any defects repaired and tested by a competent person. Supply cables should be handled only if the power is switched off.

24.3.15. Seafarers should be aware that a container may drop as a result of failure of cargo handling equipment and that the structure of a container itself may fail due to overloading or damage during cargo operations. This may result in the contents of the container spilling out and raining down on deck. Seafarers transiting the deck during cargo operations should, if possible, use the outboard side of the vessel.

24.3.16. Seafarers should wear the appropriate protective equipment when on deck in the vicinity of containers. They should be aware that loose lashing gear, particularly twistlocks and lashing gear inadvertently dropped during cargo operations, pose a considerable danger.

24.3.17. All deck areas and the tops of containers should be checked for loose lashing gear after cargo operations have been completed.

24.3.18. If a container is leaking, the content of the cargo should at first be established from its placarding and from the documentation carried on board ship. The provisions of Chapter 7 should be followed.

24.3.19. Intermodal freight containers should be hoisted only vertically and with the aid of the correct spreader.

24.3.20. Under no circumstances should containers be lifted with the aid of wire slings alone, as deformation of the container may occur which renders it unsuitable for replacing in cell guides and/or handling by specialized equipment.

24.4. Ro-Ros (roll-on/roll-off vessels) and vehicle and passenger ferries

24.4.1. Seafarers should receive special training as required, especially in the operation and maintenance of ramps and vehicle access doors.

24.4.2. Ships should be provided with a cargo securing manual.

24.4.3. Special attention should be paid to the possible ingress of water, for example, through defective door closures, scuppers, broken bilge pipes and faulty bilge non-return valves, which may affect the stability of the ship. Any water that does enter should be pumped out as soon as possible.

24.4.4. The master should ensure that an effective system of supervision and reporting of the closing and opening of doors and ramps is in operation. Doors should never be open when the ship is under way.

24.4.5. The appropriate gas detection instruments should be carried on board to check if ro-ro spaces are gas-free (see Chapter 10).

24.4.6. The advice given in operating manuals should be followed when opening, working, closing, locking and maintaining cargo access equipment.

24.4.7. Vehicles should be provided with the requisite number of securing points to enable the cargo to be properly secured to withstand the forces, particularly the transverse forces, which may arise during the voyage.

24.4.8. Ships should be provided with fixed cargo securing arrangements and with portable securing gear, the correct application of which should be described in the ship's cargo handling manual.

24.4.9. Shippers' advice or guidelines on handling, loading, stowing and lashing individual cargo units should be observed.

24.4.10. Before being accepted for shipment, every freight vehicle should be inspected externally by a responsible person to check that it is in satisfactory condition for shipment. Cargo units or vehicles should not be accepted for shipment if there is reason to suspect that:

(a) cargo has been packaged or stowed in an unsatisfactory way;

(b) a vehicle is in a bad state of repair or overloaded;

(c) the unit itself cannot be safely stowed or secured to the ship and may therefore pose a danger to ship, cargo and crew;

(d) the unit might contain dangerous goods;

(e) the unit is not properly marked.

24.4.11. The type and number of lashings per vehicle depends on the stowage space within the ship and the dimensions and the weight of the vehicle.

24.4.12. The movement, stowage and securing of vehicles should be well planned and carried out by at least two competent persons. Adequate means of communication (e.g. hand-held radios) should be used when possible.

24.4.13. Ships' ramps, car platforms, retractable car-decks and similar equipment should be operated only by competent persons authorized by a competent officer. Safe systems of work should be provided to ensure that the safety and health of persons are not put at risk when the equipment is operated.

24.4.14. Passengers and drivers should not be permitted to remain on vehicle decks without the express authority of a competent officer. Prominent notices should be displayed in vehicles spaces and passenger accommodation to bring this restriction to the attention of passengers and drivers. The period prior to disembarkation, when passengers and drivers are requested to return to their vehicles, should be kept to a minimum.

24.4.15. Ramps used by vehicles should not be used for pedestrian access unless there is suitable separation of vehicles and pedestrians.

24.4.16. Where permanent walkways are provided on vehicle decks, they should be adequate in extent, safe to use, and clearly marked and signposted.

24.4.17. Suitable notices or appropriate instructions should be made to inform persons on vehicle decks of the dangers from moving vehicles and of the need to exercise extreme caution to minimize the risk to health and safety.

24.4.18. Seafarers working on vehicle decks should wear suitable high visibility garments.

24.4.19. Seafarers should exercise great care when supervising the driving, marshalling, stowing and securing of vehicles to ensure that no person is put at risk.

24.4.20. No attempt should be made to secure a vehicle until it is parked, the brakes have been applied and the engine switched off.

24.4.21. Hand lamps and torches should be available wherever seafarers are working in poorly lit areas or have to go under vehicles to secure lashings.

24.4.22. Seafarers engaged in the securing of vehicles should take care to avoid injury from projections on the underside of vehicles.

24.4.23. Lashings and their points of attachment should be regularly checked during the voyage and retightened when necessary. Persons inspecting vehicle spaces during a voyage should exercise caution to avoid being injured by moving or swaying vehicles. If necessary, the ship's course should be altered to reduce movement when lashings are being adjusted. The officer of the watch should always be informed whenever an inspection of the vehicle deck is being carried out.

24.4.24. To reduce the build-up of fumes, for example carbon monoxide, drivers should be instructed to stop their engines as soon as practicable after embarking and to avoid starting up prior to departure until instructed to do so. Warning notices to this effect should be posted at the entrances to and within vehicle spaces. The appropriate national and international requirements with respect to ventilation should be observed. Where there is doubt about the quality of the air, arrangements should be made for testing (see also Chapter 10 and paragraph 24.4.5). The car deck should be ventilated in accordance with the ship's ventilation plan.

24.4.25. Noise levels on vehicle decks should be monitored and appropriate hearing protection made available.

24.4.26. Smoking should not be permitted on the vehicle deck.

24.4.27. If the presence of flammable vapour is suspected or detected, all electrical circuits and items of equipment that are not intrinsically safe, or certified flame-proof, should be isolated from a position outside the space. Seafarers and passengers should not be allowed into the space until the vapour has been effectively dispersed.

24.4.28. All vehicle decks, ships' ramps and lifting appliances should be kept free of water, grease, oil, or any liquid which might cause a person to slip or fall.

24.4.29. Drums, canisters, fuel, gas and acetylene cylinders should not be stowed on the vehicle deck.[1]

24.4.30. Retractable car-decks and lifting appliances should be securely locked when in the stowed position.

24.4.31. No vehicle movements should occur until the ferry has been made fast to the dock.

24.4.32. Particular attention should be paid to vehicles, unit load and trucks carrying dangerous goods.[2] The goods carried and full safety information should be specified on the relevant transit document of the vehicle. Care should be taken to ensure that the proper separation from other vehicles, or from other substances carried in other vehicles, is maintained. The guidance of Chapter 7 should be observed.

24.5. Oil tankers

24.5.1. This section deals with both crude and product tankers.

---

[1] Reference should be made to IMO Resolution A.489(XII).
[2] IMDG Code.

24.5.2. The appropriate national and international requirements should be observed.[1]

24.5.3. Particular attention is drawn to the importance of the International Safety Guide for Oil Tankers and Terminals (ISGOTT) which provides comprehensive information on the safe operation of tankers.[2]

24.5.4. Seafarers employed on tankers should be properly trained in accordance with applicable national and international requirements.

24.5.5. For each operation the master should designate a competent officer who is familiar with the safe operation of tankers. The master should ensure that the designated officer has available an adequate number of competent persons.

24.5.6. Particular attention is drawn to the following specific issues:

(a) the need for a well-structured on board safety policy backed up by the appropriate safety committee with designated responsibilities (see Chapter 2);

(b) the need for strict smoking and hot-work policies;

(c) the need for crew members to fully understand the hazardous nature of cargoes carried;

(d) the need for crew members to be aware of the precautions necessary to enter an enclosed space (see Chapter 10);

---

[1] In particular the SOLAS Convention, Chapter II-2, Part D, regulations 59, 60, 62 and 63 and, for marine pollution matters, MARPOL 73/78, Annex I. Because of limitations in space, this code does not go into detail on MARPOL or other pollution requirements. Nevertheless, they are essential and should be observed.

[2] Consideration should also be given to providing seafarers with copies of the ICS *Safety in Oil Tankers*.

(e)   the need for crew members to be aware of the inherent dangers of cargo pumprooms. Pumprooms, by virtue of their location, design and operation, constitute a particular hazard and therefore necessitate special precautions;

(f)   the need for crew members to be made aware of the carcinogenic health hazards resulting from exposure to minor concentrations of benzene vapour in the air.[1] This hazard can result from breathing vapours of benzene-containing cargoes such as gasolenes, JP-4 and some crude oils;

(g)   the need to ensure that seafarers are made aware of the safety precautions and emergency action to be taken in the event of spillage.

24.6. Bulk chemical tankers

24.6.1. Aspects of section 24.5 may also apply to this section.

24.6.2. Ships intended for the carriage of chemicals in bulk should comply with the appropriate national and international regulations.[2]

24.6.3. Ships intended for the carriage of chemicals should carry only those chemicals for which their construction and equipment are suitable, and which are specified on the certificate of fitness.

24.6.4. Particular attention is drawn to the importance of the Tanker Safety Guide (Chemicals) which provides comprehensive information on the safe operation of chemical tankers.[3]

---

[1] ILO Benzene Convention, 1971 (No. 136), and Recommendation, 1971 (No. 144).

[2] The IMO's *International Code for the Construction and Equipment of Ships Carrying Chemicals in Bulk* (BCH code) should be consulted.

[3] The International Chamber of Shipping publication *Safety in Chemical Tankers* is also useful, particularly for ratings.

24.6.5. Seafarers employed on chemical tankers should receive specialized training and be instructed in the safe carriage of all chemicals which the ship may be required to carry, as appropriate to their duties.

24.6.6. For each operation the master should designate a competent officer who is familiar with the safe operation of tankers. The master should ensure that the designated officer has available an adequate number of suitably trained and experienced seafarers.

24.6.7. Particular attention is drawn to the following specific issues:

(a) the need to ensure that any cargo offered is listed in the shipping documents by the correct technical name;

(b) the need to ensure that where a cargo is a mixture, an analysis is provided indicating the dangerous components which contribute significantly to the hazard of the product. This information should be available on board, and be freely accessible to all concerned;

(c) the need to ensure that a full description of a cargo's physical and chemical properties is supplied with each cargo loaded;

(d) the need to ensure that seafarers are made aware of the safety precautions and emergency action to be taken in the event of spillage or crew exposure to possible contamination by chemicals;

(e) the need to ensure that cargoes requiring stabilizers or inhibitors, and which are not accompanied by the required certificates, are not accepted for shipment;

(f) the need to carry out emergency drills using protective equipment and safety and rescue devices at regular intervals;

(g) the need to plan effective first-aid treatment in the event of accidental personal contact.[1]

---

[1] The *Medical first-aid guide for use in accidents involving dangerous goods* should be consulted.

24.7. Liquefied natural and petroleum gas carriers

24.7.1. Aspects of section 24.5 may also apply to this section.

24.7.2. The appropriate national and international requirements should be observed.[1]

24.7.3. Ships intended for the carriage of liquefied gas should carry only those liquids for which its construction and equipment are suitable, and which are specified on the certificate of fitness.

24.7.4. Particular attention is drawn to the importance of the Tanker Safety Guide (Liquefied Gas)[2] and the Liquefied Gas Handling Principles on Ships and in Terminals,[3] which provides comprehensive information on the safe operation of liquefied gas carriers.

24.7.5. Seafarers employed on liquefied gas carriers should be properly trained in accordance with applicable national and international requirements.

24.7.6. Comprehensive operating instructions should be provided concerning the particular ship and cargo.

24.7.7. For each operation the master should designate a competent officer who is familiar with the safe operation of liquefied gas carriers. The master should ensure that the designated officer has available an adequate number of competent persons.

24.7.8. Particular attention is drawn to the following specific issues:

---

[1] National requirements should, at a minimum, comply with the IMO's International *Code for the Construction and Equipment of Ships Carrying Liquefied Gases in Bulk (IGC code)*.

[2] *The Tanker Safety Guide (liquefied gas)* (ICS latest edition).

[3] *The Liquefied Gas Handling Principles on Ships and in Terminals* (SIGTTO, 1986 or latest edition).

(a) the need to ensure that a full description of the cargo's physical and chemical properties is supplied with each cargo loaded;

(b) the need to ensure that seafarers are made aware of the safety precautions and emergency action to be taken in the event of spillage;

(c) the need to plan effective first aid treatment due to possible physical contact with liquefied gases or cold cryogenic pipelines, some of which can be at a temperature of minus 160 centigrade;

(d) the need to carry out emergency drills at regular intervals using personal protective equipment and safety and rescue devices.

24.8. Passenger vessels[1]

24.8.1. The IMO Convention for the Safety of Life at Sea (SOLAS) requires a sufficient number of trained persons to be on board for mustering and assisting untrained persons.

24.8.2. Personnel nominated on muster lists to assist passengers in emergency situations should receive additional training to enable them to perform their duties properly. The number of trained persons should always be sufficient to assist the total number of passengers who may be on board at any one time. The number of trained persons should be included on the ship's safe manning document.

24.8.3. Where training is given in a shore-based training course, it should be supplemented by shipboard training before assuming the duties referred to in 24.8.2. The training should be to the satisfaction of the flag State and some means should be established of

---

[1] Reference should be made to the following: SOLAS (1974, as amended), Chapter III; IMO Resolution A.691(17), Safety Instructions to Passengers; and IMO Resolution A.770(18), 1993, Minimum Training Requirements for Personnel Nominated to Assist Passengers in Emergency Situations on Passenger Ships; IMO Resolution A.792(19), Safety Culture in and around Passenger Ships.

ensuring that crew members maintain continued proficiency through periodic refresher training, drills or related work experience.

24.8.4. The communication skills of the nominated seafarers should be sufficient to assist passengers during an emergency, taking into account the following criteria:

(a) the language or languages appropriate to the principal nationalities of passengers carried on a particular route;

(b) the likelihood that an ability to use elementary English vocabulary for basic instructions can provide a means of communicating with a passenger in need of assistance whether or not the passenger and crew member share a common language;

(c) the possible need to communicate during an emergency by some other means (e.g. by demonstration, or hand signals, or calling attention to the location of instructions, muster stations, life-saving devices or evacuation routes) when verbal communication is impractical;

(d) the extent to which complete safety instructions have been provided to passengers in their native language or languages; and

(e) the languages in which emergency announcements may be broadcast during an emergency or drill to convey critical guidance to passengers and to help crew members in assisting passengers.

24.8.5. The training provided under 24.8.2 should include but not necessarily be limited to the following theoretical and practical items:

(a) awareness of life-saving appliance plans and fire-control plans, and knowledge of muster lists and emergency instructions including:

(i) general alarms and procedures for mustering of passengers;

(ii) areas of responsibility with emphasis on "own section";

(b) general layout of the ship with special emphasis on location of muster and embarkation stations, accesses and escape routes;

(c) location and use of emergency equipment relevant to the duties in 24.8.2 with emphasis on "own section" and escape routes therefrom;

(d) location of adult and infant lifejackets;

(e) location of other evacuation supplies, e.g. blankets, to be taken to survival craft;

(f) elementary first aid and transportation of casualties;

(g) communication:

    (i) the use of internal communication systems;

   (ii) raising the alarm;

  (iii) alerting the passengers;

  (iv) reporting and notification;

(h) evacuation:

    (i) the use of passenger lists or counts;

   (ii) the alarm signals;

  (iii) mustering; importance of keeping order and panic avoidance procedures;

  (iv) emergency exits;

   (v) evacuation equipment;

  (vi) control of passengers in corridors, staircases and passageways;

 (vii) maintenance of escape routes clear of obstructions;

(viii) assistance en route to muster and embarkation station;

  (ix) methods available for evacuation of disabled persons and persons needing special assistance;

   (x) restrictions on the use of elevators;

  (xi) search of accommodation spaces;

  (xii) ensuring that the passengers are suitably clothed and have
         donned their lifejackets correctly;

(i) fire situations:

    (i) fire detection and initial containment;

    (ii) raising the alarm;

    (iii) danger of smoke inhalation;

    (iv) breathing protection;

(j) abandon ship situations:

    (i) correct use of individual survival equipment, e.g. life-
         jackets, immersion suits, lifebuoys, light and smoke
         signals, etc.;

    (ii) need for assistance to special cases;

(k) familiarization by means of repeated organized guided tours on
     board;

(l) repeated participation in fire drills and lifeboat drills including
     transportation of simulated casualties;

(m) repeated exercise in use of equipment, such as donning of
     lifejackets and appropriate protective clothing;

(n) repeated exercise in use of internal communication systems;

(o) repeated exercises in evacuation.

24.8.6. Before the vessel leaves port, instructions should be
issued to passengers on emergency and evacuation procedures.

24.8.7. Where possible a short safety video should be screened
shortly after embarkation of passengers.

24.8.8. Unambiguous emergency signs to assist passengers
should be placed at the appropriate level and should be in a language
understood by a majority of passengers, indicating paths to muster
stations and the location of lifejacket containers. The IMO international symbols should be used for this purpose.

24.8.9. Lifeboat drills should be carried out in compliance with SOLAS and other life-saving appliances and equipment should be examined regularly and kept in good order. The manufacturers' instructions with respect to maintenance and replacement should always be followed.

24.8.10. Klaxon and communications systems should be tested regularly and kept in good working order.

24.8.11. Man-overboard drills and procedures should be conducted regularly.

24.9. Offshore support vessels

Introduction

24.9.1. Offshore support vessels were not, at the time of preparing this code, subject to specific international regulation with regard to seafarers' safety and health. The provisions of this code therefore reflect elements of best practice drawn from national and other codes in the course of preparation. Where support vessels are required to carry out the duties of a standby vessel, due consideration should be given to the national and international requirements for this type of vessel.[1]

Cargo handling

24.9.2. (1) Where appropriate, all containers, baskets, etc., should be preslung with a four-leg ring arrangement terminating in a single ring with pennant line.

---

[1] STCW 1978; and the publication coedited by the Department of Transport and the Health and Safety Executive, *Assessment of the suitability of stand-by vessels attending offshore installations: Instructions for the guidance of surveyors* (London, Her Majesty's Stationery Office, 1991).

(2) Container doors should be adequately secured and a means to prevent dislodging of the door-securing mechanism provided.

(3) The use of boat-shaped skips should be strongly discouraged.

(4) Open cargo baskets containing loose equipment or rubbish should be provided with safety nets to retain the contents.

(5) Multiple stacking as one unit should be discouraged. To avoid the need for seafarers to climb into a skip or open basket or on top of containers, the lifting gear shall be of sufficient length to enable connection at deck level.

(6) As much cargo as possible should be in containers, to allow for safer stowage and securing on deck.

Responsibilities

24.9.3. When carrying out cargo operations, the responsibility for the safety of the crew and vessel rests with the master at all times. The master should consider whether any ongoing operation should continue or cease, and should question any instruction received from the installation which may create a hazard to his crew or vessel.

24.9.4. Shipowners should ensure that vessels are manned by seafarers with the necessary experience and competence. An induction course for seafarers new to working on offshore support vessels should be provided. Where circumstances permit, deck officers should be trained on board in relevant ship-handling operations.

Cargo planning

24.9.5. The order of loading, discharging and stowage arrangements should be pre-planned to avoid the "slotting in" of containers and the necessity for the potentially dangerous practice of seafarers climbing on top of the cargo. Before loading, the master should be given details of any unusual items of cargo, cargo which requires special sea fastening arrangements, or heavy lifts.

24.9.6. The master should be warned in good time of expected tubular backloads, to plan appropriate stowage in advance. Tubular cargoes should be pre-slung in bundles or singly and secured by bulldog grips or other equivalent methods to prevent slippage.

Cargo restraint

24.9.7. Cargo should always be restrained, and restraints should be in position before the vessel sails and remain in position during the voyage. In deciding the type of restraining arrangements appropriate, the master should take into account the motion characteristics of the vessel, the anticipated weather, the freeboard, the nature of the cargo and the number of installations to be worked. Where fitted, pipe posts should be used to restrain the movement of tubulars.

Crane operations

24.9.8. In all cargo work, in port and offshore, crane drivers should have a clear view of the vessel's deck. If he cannot see the deck then a seafarer should be appointed for signalling duties. For offshore crane operations a safety pennant of sufficient length should be provided between either the headache ball or floating block and the hook both of which should be illuminated. The use of swivel, self-locking safety hooks are strongly recommended.

24.9.9. Operations involving heavy lifts require reasonable weather. Other operations, such as bulk handling etc., may have to be suspended whilst heavy lifts are handled. Taglines should be attached to heavy or large lifts to aid lifting.

Master/Offshore Installation Manager (OIM) information exchange

24.9.10. Before starting cargo operations, the programme should be discussed and agreed by radio between the OIM and the master, or their appointed deputies, to ensure that the installation and vessel are ready in all respects. Excessive waiting time alongside the installation should be avoided.

Communications

24.9.11. Effective communications should be set up between the master, the installation staff and the seafarers, and competent persons should be proficient in the appropriate language. A radio communication link on a dedicated channel should be maintained at all times during the cargo operation.

Installation overboard discharges

24.9.12. All non-essential installation overboard discharges which could hamper safe vessel operations alongside the installation should be shut down before the cargo operations start. Where an installation overboard discharge presents a hazard to the safety or health of seafarers, the master should cease operations and stand off until the discharge has stopped or prevailing conditions keep the discharge clear of the vessel.

Bulk transfer procedures

24.9.13. The following procedures should be used before and during any transfer offshore of bulk cargo to or from a vessel:

(a) the estimated pumping rate for each product, the length of warning/estimate of time required to stop, the emergency stop procedure and confirmation that lines can be drained back to the vessel's tanks where necessary should be confirmed;

(b) the master should be informed of the size of hoses and connections to be used, the length of hose available, the colour scheme in operation for the hose and/or product, the maximum loading rate/pressure permitted, and the quantities of each product required, the order in which they are required and an estimate of the time at which they will be required;

(c) where conditions are suitable, the crane should be used to lift the hose to aid draining. On disconnecting the hose, the end should be fitted with a cap or blank. Hoses for potable/fresh water should not be used for bulk and other liquid cargoes. Sufficient illumination should be provided over the hose and support vessel throughout the operation. For operations during hours of darkness, hoses should be fitted with high visibility bands or tape;

(d) hoses are normally colour coded for manufacturers' identification and approval, frequently by the use of spiral coloured bands within the hose structure. The hose terminations should be colour coded by use of a coloured band to mark the product, for example:

  – potable water – blue
  – drill water – green
  – fuel – brown
  – brine – black.

24.9.14. Passing hoses to vessels is a hazardous operation and it should be supervised by a responsible person on the installation with direct communication to the vessel's master. Continuous radio communication with the installation should be maintained whilst a vessel is connected to bulk hoses and the crane driver should remain in his cab. Relevant installation personnel should stand by appropriate valves so as to act quickly in the event of an emergency.

Anchor handling/towing operations

24.9.15. Rig anchor handling at sea can be a particularly arduous and hazardous task for which many variable factors apply, thus preventing laying down formal guidance. Seafarers should be aware of the operational limitations of their vessel, including the individual power and freeboard, with their safety and health being of paramount importance. Shipowners should ensure that vessels involved in anchor handling and their equipment are fit for the purpose and are adequately manned by efficient seafarers with the relevant experience. Where manning levels are minimum, the need for additional crew should be considered. Trainees should only be used as supernumeries.

24.9.16. To maintain safe working conditions on anchor handling vessels the following should be considered:

(a) the use of a safe and effective method of stoppering wire pennants in mechanical stoppers;

(b) the operation and maintenance of all equipment to be in accordance with manufacturer's instructions;

(c) the use of a system for testing, inspection, maintenance and recording of anchor handling equipment retained on board vessels and installations;

(d) the susceptibility to excessive wear of soft eye pendants, where used. Frequent inspection of these is recommended;

(e) the monitoring of the use of roller fairlead mounted on the deck or crash barrier of vessels. Inspection and maintenance should be performed regularly so as to ensure that any uplift by external forces, such as a tugger wire, are not liable to dislodge roller fairleads from their seating;

(f) the careful handling of wire coils when opened up, in particular pendant wires, which may cause injury by the sudden springing open of the coils following release of the securing bands;

(g) the securing of all equipment, including that used in anchor handling operations, until required.

24.9.17. Competent persons should be proficient in the appropriate language, as effective communications between the master, the seafarers and the installation are essential for safety. An effective radio communication link on a dedicated channel should be maintained at all times whilst the vessel is engaged in anchor handling and/or towing operations, and, due to the nature of the operation, it is recommended that a dedicated VHF working channel is identified purely for anchor handling and/or towing operations.

24.9.18. Offshore installation personnel should ensure that whenever pennants are passed to vessels close alongside, crane drivers are experienced in this operation, effective communication has established agreed procedures for the pennant transfer, and adequate supervision is available. When running anchors, the anchor-handling master should be advised where the installation winches have payout limitations, so that speed can be controlled. Effective communication should be established between the master and the winch driver.

24.9.19. A safe method of passing the main towing pennant from the installation to the towing vessel should be established, with a clear understanding of the procedures to be used by all parties. The secondary towing system on an installation must be identified, method of retrieval of the main towing gear established, and safe method of passing the secondary towing system agreed. Towing vessels should ensure that the installation personnel are aware of the time that may be required to rig their spare towing wire. When an additional vessel is available as reserve tug whilst on passage, it should be rigged for towing. When towing, a towing sleeve should be fitted to the main towing line to prevent chafing.

Transfer of seafarers by boat

24.9.20. The following should be observed when the transfer of seafarers by boat takes place:

(a) there should be an efficient means of communication between the ship and the installation which should be maintained throughout the operation;

(b) the master of the ship providing the boat should be responsible for the operation. Due consideration should be given to sea and weather conditions and their effect upon the safety of the mission;

(c) the boat should be reliably powered and manned by not less than two competent persons;

(d) suitable protective clothing and life-jackets should be worn by crew and those seafarers being transferred;

(e) safety ropes should be provided for all persons boarding and leaving the boat. This exercise should be carried out in an orderly manner. There should be no standing in the boat and people should seat themselves as directed by the coxswain.

Transfer of seafarers by basket

24.9.21. Transfer of seafarers from vessel to installation by personnel basket should only be carried out as a last resort and with the express agreement of the individual concerned. Due regard should be paid to seafarers who suffer from a fear of heights.

24.9.22. Where it is necessary to transfer seafarers by basket the following procedures should be observed:

(a) there should be an efficient means of communication between the vessel and the installation, which should be maintained throughout the operation;

(b) the master of the vessel should be responsible for the operation. Due consideration should be given to sea and weather conditions and their effect upon the operation;

(c) at least two seafarers should steady the basket when it is lowered to the deck;

(d) seafarers to be transferred should wear protective clothing and life jackets;

(e) seafarers transferring should distribute themselves evenly around the baseboard to ensure maximum stability;

(f) any luggage should be secured inside the net of the basket;

(g) the master should instruct the crane operator to slew the crane jib away from the vessel whilst lifting the personnel basket.

Appendices

Appendix I Permit-to-work form[1]

Note: The responsible officer should indicate the sections applicable by marks in the left-hand spaces next to the headings, and by deleting any subheading not applicable. The officer should insert the appropriate details when the sections for Other work *or* Additional precautions *are used.*

The person in charge of the work should mark each applicable right-hand space when completing each check.

Work to be done ————————————————————————

Period of validity of permit ——————————————————

Location ——————————————————————————

Person in charge of the work ————————————————

Persons performing the work ————————————————

Responsible officer *(signature)* ————————————————

Date ——————————————— Time ————————————

Master's signature ————————————————————————

Date ——————————————— Time ————————————

Entry into enclosed or confined spaces

———————   Space thoroughly ventilated   ———————

———————   Atmosphere tested and found safe   ———————

———————   Rescue and resuscitation equipment available at entrance   ———————

———————   Responsible person in attendance at entrance   ———————

---

[1] Based upon the form found in the Department of Transport's *Code of safe working practices for merchant seamen* (London, HMSO, 1991).

Accident prevention on board ship

———— Communication arrangements made between person at entrance ————
and those entering

———— Access and illumination adequate ————

———— All equipment to be used is of an approved type ————

———— When breathing apparatus is to be used:

(1) familiarity of user with apparatus is confirmed ————

(2) apparatus has been tested and found to be satisfactory ————

Machinery or equipment

———— Removed from service/isolated from sources of power or heat ————

———— All relevant personnel informed ————

———— Warning notices displayed ————

Hot work

———— Area clear of dangerous material and gas-free ————

———— Ventilation adequate ————

———— Equipment in good order ————

———— Fire appliances in good order ————

Other work

———— ———————————————————————— ————

———— ———————————————————————— ————

———— ———————————————————————— ————

Additional precautions

———— ———————————————————————— ————

———— ———————————————————————— ————

———— ———————————————————————— ————

Certificate of checks

———— ———————————————————————————————— ————

———— ———————————————————————————————— ————

———— ———————————————————————————————— ————

     I am satisfied that all precautions have been taken and that safety arrangements will be maintained for the duration of the work.

(Signature of person in charge) ————————————————————————————

Certificate of completion

     The work has been completed and all persons under my supervision, materials and equipment have been withdrawn.

(Signature of person in charge) ————————————————————————————

(Date) —————————————————— (Time) ——————————————————

Appendix II References and further reading[1]

ILO instruments

Maritime instruments

Minimum Age (Sea) Convention, 1920 (No. 7)

Labour Inspection (Seamen) Recommendation, 1926 (No. 28)

Officers' Competency Certificates Convention, 1936 (No. 53)

Minimum Age (Sea) Convention (Revised), 1936 (No. 58)

Food and Catering (Ships' Crews) Convention, 1946 (No. 68)

Certification of Ships' Cooks Convention, 1946 (No. 69)

Certification of Able Seamen Convention, 1946 (No. 74)

Bedding, Mess Utensils and Miscellaneous Provisions (Ships' Crews) Recommendation, 1946 (No. 78)

Accommodation of Crews Convention (Revised), 1949 (No. 92)

Ships' Medicine Chests Recommendation, 1958 (No. 105)

Medical Advice at Sea Recommendation, 1958 (No. 106)

Wages, Hours of Work and Manning (Sea) Convention (Revised), 1958 (No. 109)

---

[1] International instruments, resolutions, codes and guidelines, whether developed by intergovernmental or non-governmental organizations, are periodically revised, amended or otherwise updated. The most recent applicable publication or publications should be used.

Accommodation of Crews (Supplementary Provisions) Convention, 1970 (No. 133)

Prevention of Accidents (Seafarers) Convention, 1970 (No. 134)

Vocational Training (Seafarers) Recommendation, 1970 (No. 137)

Crew Accommodation (Air Conditioning) Recommendation, 1970 (No. 140)

Crew Accommodation (Noise Control) Recommendation, 1970 (No. 141)

Prevention of Accidents (Seafarers) Recommendation, 1970 (No. 142)

Protection of Young Seafarers Recommendation, 1976 (No. 153)

Merchant Shipping (Minimum Standards) Convention, 1976 (No. 147)

Merchant Shipping (Improvement of Standards) Recommendation, 1976 (No. 155)

Health Protection and Medical Care (Seafarers) Convention, 1987 (No. 164)

Occupational safety and health instruments

General provisions

Occupational Safety and Health Convention, 1981 (No. 155)

Occupational Safety and Health Recommendation, 1981 (No. 164)

Protection against specific risks

Anthrax Prevention Recommendation, 1919 (No. 3)

White Lead (Painting) Convention, 1921 (No. 13)

Radiation Protection Convention, 1960 (No. 115)

Radiation Protection Recommendation, 1960 (No. 114)

Benzene Convention, 1971 (No. 136)

Benzene Recommendation, 1971 (No. 144)

Occupational Cancer Convention, 1974 (No. 139)

Occupational Cancer Recommendation, 1974 (No. 147)

Machinery

Guarding of Machinery Convention, 1963 (No. 119)

Guarding of Machinery Recommendation, 1963 (No. 118)

Maximum weight

Maximum Weight Convention, 1967 (No. 127)

Maximum Weight Recommendation, 1967 (No. 128)

Air pollution, noise and vibration

Working Environment (Air Pollution, Noise and Vibration) Convention, 1977 (No. 148)

Working Environment (Air Pollution, Noise and Vibration) Recommendation, 1977 (No. 156)

Dock work

Marking of Weight (Packages Transported by Vessels) Convention, 1929 (No. 27)

Protection against Accidents (Dockers) Convention, 1929 (No. 28)

Protection against Accidents (Dockers) Convention (Revised), 1932 (No. 32)

Occupational Safety and Health (Dock Work) Convention, 1979 (No. 152)

Occupational Safety and Health (Dock Work) Recommendation, 1979 (No. 160)

Health insurance

Medical Care and Sickness Benefits Convention, 1969 (No. 130)

ILO occupational safety and health publications

Codes of practice

Occupational exposure to airborne substances harmful to health (Geneva, 1980).

Safety and health in dock work (Geneva, 2nd ed., 1977).

Safety in the use of asbestos (Geneva, 1984).

Protection of workers against noise and vibration in the working environment (Geneva, 1984).

Management of drug- and alcohol-related issues in the workplace (in preparation).

Occupational safety and health series

Occupational exposure limits for airborne toxic substances (Geneva, 3rd ed., 1991) – OSH No. 37.

Safe use of pesticides: Guidelines (Geneva, 1985) – OSH No. 38.

The provisions of the basic safety standards for radiation protection relevant to the protection of workers against ionizing radiation (Geneva, 1985) – OSH No. 55.

Protection of workers against radio frequency and microwave radiation: A technical review (Geneva, 1986) – OSH No. 57.

Maximum weights in load lifting and carrying (Geneva, 1988) – OSH No. 59.

Working with visual display units (Geneva, 1990) – OSH No. 61.

Guides and manuals

Guide to safety and health in dock work (Geneva, 1976).

Safety and health in the use of chemicals at work: A training manual (Geneva, ILO, 1993).

Guiding principles on drug and alcohol testing procedures for worldwide application in the maritime industry (Geneva, ILO/WHO, 1993).

Drugs and alcohol in the maritime industry, Report of the ILO Interregional Meeting of Experts, Geneva, Sep.-Oct. 1992 (Geneva, ILO, 1993).

Drug and alcohol testing in the workplace, Report of the ILO Interregional Tripartite Experts Meeting, Oslo, May 1993 (Geneva, ILO, 1994).

Drug and alcohol prevention programmes in the maritime industry: A manual for planners (Geneva, ILO, forthcoming).

IMO instruments

International Convention for the Prevention of Pollution from Ships (MARPOL), 1973.

International Convention on Standards of Training, Certification and Watchkeeping for Seafarers (STCW), 1978. [Amended in 1995]

International Convention for the Safety of Life at Sea (SOLAS), 1986.

IMO publications

Code of safe practice for cargo storage and securing (London, 1992).

Code of safe practice for ships carrying timber deck cargoes (London, 1992).

Code of safe practice for solid bulk cargoes (BC Code) (London, 1991).

Comprehensive Index of Valid Technical Guidelines and Recommendations (London, latest edition).

Emergency procedures for ships carrying dangerous goods (EmS) (London, 1991).

International code for the safe carriage of grain in bulk (International Grain Code) (London, 1991).

International Convention for Safe Containers (CSC) (London, 1992).

International Convention for the Prevention of Pollution from Ships, 1973, as modified by the Protocol of 1978 (MARPOL 73/78), consolidated edition (London, 1991, or later revision).

International Convention for the Safety of Life at Sea (SOLAS) (London, latest consolidated text).

International Convention on Standards of Training, Certification and Watchkeeping for Seafarers (STCW 1978) (London, latest revision and amendments. [A new edition, entitled *International Convention on Standards of Training, Certification and Watchkeeping for Seafarers, 1978, as amended in 1995* (STCW 1995) was published in 1996, also containing the *Seafarer's Training, Certification and Watchkeeping Code*].

International maritime dangerous goods code (IMDG Code) (London, 1990).

IMO/ILO Document for guidance: An international maritime training guide, 1985 (London, 1987) (or latest edition).

Medical first-aid guide for use in accidents involving dangerous goods (MFAG) (London, IMO/WHO/ILO, 1991).

Merchant Ship Search and Rescue Manual (MERSAR Manual) (London, 1993 or later revision).

Recommendations on the safe use of pesticides in ships (London, 1981).

WHO publications

International medical guide for ships

UN publications

Bulletin on Narcotics, Vol. XLV, No. 2, 1993 (New York, UNDCP, 1994).

Industry publications

Effective mooring (London, Oil Companies International Marine Forum (OCIMF), 1989).

Guide to helicopter/ship operations (London, International Chamber of Shipping (ICS), 3rd ed., 1989).

International safety guide for oil tankers and terminals (ISGOTT) (London, ICS, OCIMF and International Association of Ports and Harbours, 3rd ed., 1988, revised 1991).

Safety in chemical tankers (London, ICS, 1977).

Safety in liquefied gas tankers (London, ICS, 1980).

Safety in oil tankers (London, ICS, 1978).

Tanker safety guide (chemicals) (London, ICS, 2nd ed., 1992).

Tanker safety guide (liquefied gas) (London, ICS, 2nd ed., 1991).

The management of safety in shipping (London, Nautical Institute, 1991).

Other publications

Code of safe working practices for merchant seamen, Department of Transport (London, HMSO, 1991).

Roll-on/roll-off ships – Stowage and securing of vehicles – Code of practice (London, HMSO, 1991).

Where to obtain information

International Labour Office (ILO)
Publications Bureau
4, route des Morillons
CH-1211 GENEVA 22
Switzerland

World Health Organization (WHO)
Avenue Appia
CH-1211 GENEVA 27
Switzerland

International Maritime Organization (IMO)
Publications Section
4 Albert Embankment
LONDON SE1 7SR
United Kingdom

International Chamber of Shipping (ICS)
Carthusian Court
12 Carthusian Street
LONDON EC1M 6EB
United Kingdom

Oil Companies International Marine Forum (OCIMF)
15th Floor
Esso House
96 Victoria Street
LONDON SW1E 1BH
United Kingdom

International Association of Dry Cargo Shipowners (Intercargo)
17 Bell Court House
11-12 Bloomfield Street
LONDON EC2M 7AY
United Kingdom

International Shipping Federation (ISF)
Carthusian Court
12 Carthusian Street
LONDON EC1M 6EB
United Kingdom

International Transport Workers' Federation (ITF)
49-60 Borough Road
LONDON SE1 1DS
United Kingdom

Society of International Gas Tanker and Terminal Operators Ltd. (SIGTTO)
91 Worship Street
LONDON EC2A 2BE
United Kingdom

International Ship Managers Association (ISMA)
Carthusian Court
12 Carthusian Street
LONDON EC1M 6EB
United Kingdom

International Association of Independent Tanker Owners (INTERTANKO)
Gange-Rolvs Gate 5
OSLO 2
Norway

Nautical Institute
202 Lambeth Road
LONDON SE1 7LQ
United Kingdom

International Organization for Standardization (ISO)
Case postale 56
1, rue de Varembé
CH-1211 GENEVA 20
Switzerland

Appendix III   ISO Standards

ISO 6812:1983   Roll on/Roll off ship-to-shore connection – Interface between terminals and ships with straight stern/bow ramps.

ISO 9367-1:1989   Lashing and securing arrangements on road vehicles for sea transportation on Ro/Ro ships – General requirements – Part 1: Commercial vehicles and combinations of vehicles, semi-trailers excluded.

ISO/DIS 9367-2   Lashing and securing arrangements on road vehicles for sea transportation on Ro/Ro ships – General requirements – Part 2: Semi-trailers.

ISO 3874:1988   Series 1 freight containers – Handling and securing

ISO 8468:1990   Ship's bridge layout and associated equipment – Requirements and guidelines.

ISO 8383:1985   Lifts on ships – Specific requirements.

ISO 3864:1984   Safety colours and safety signs.

ISO 5571:1973   Shipbuilding – Identification colours for schemes for ventilation systems.

ISO 6309:1987   Fire protection – Safety signs.

ISO 6790:1986   Equipment for fire protection and fire-fighting – Graphical symbols for fire protection plans – Specification.

ISO 2801:1973   Clothing for protection against heat and fire – General recommendations for users and for those in charge of such users.

ISO 6529   Protective clothing – Protection against liquid chemicals – Determination of resistance of air-impermeable materials to permeation by liquids.

ISO 6530   Protective clothing – Protection against liquid chemicals – Determination of resistance of materials to penetration by liquids.

ISO 6942   Clothing for protection against heat and fire – Evaluation of thermal behaviour of materials and material assemblies when exposed to a source of radiant heat.

Index